The Falmouth Letters

With best wishes

Christine Woolf

Christine Woolf.

Pen Press

First published in Great Britain

All paper used in the printing of this book has been made from
wood grown in managed, sustainable forests.

ISBN13: 978-1-78003-707-3

Printed and bound in the UK
Pen Press is an imprint of
Indepenpress Publishing Limited
25 Eastern Place
Brighton
BN2 1GJ

A catalogue record of this book is available from
the British Library

Cover design by Jacqueline Abromeit

To John Woolf

Acknowledgements

Many, many thanks to Coral Pepper
and Brian and Val Hill, for hours of help and advice.

Prologue

In 1954, my father, who was a pharmacist, bought a business in Bodmin from an elderly chemist who wished to retire.

However, the Bodmin shop lacked the beautiful mahogany and glass fittings of his old shop in Derby. The furniture in the Bodmin shop consisted of a long counter and a large table on which many of the small patent medicines and advertising cards were set out. The coloured carboys in the windows, the traditional sign that I remembered so well from my earliest years, were non existent. Two old library chairs accommodated the infirm.

Sometime during the next couple of years an advertisement appeared in the Pharmaceutical Journal – the furniture, fittings and entire contents of a Falmouth pharmacy were for sale. My father applied and a price was agreed.

There followed endless journeys on Wednesday afternoons and Sundays, when the shop was shut, taking a trailer down to Falmouth and returning with racks of drawers, curved plate glass counter display cabinets, wall cabinets, carboys, bottles of every size and variety and for every purpose and even a Yardley china lavender girl group.

I missed most of these journeys as I was working in Derbyshire, but came down for the Easter holidays and helped with the final removals.

At last it seemed that we had really finished. My mother, my sister Bridget and I climbed the stairs to the attic, to make sure nothing was left behind. The attic room proved a surprise. It was furnished with a comfortable cushioned chair, a desk lamp on a table, which was pushed up against the wall. Behind the table was a cupboard. My mother, with her perennial curiosity, pulled aside the table and we opened the cupboard door.

At first we thought it was empty, but then, on a shelf we saw a box, a wooden Elliman's Embrocation box. We pulled it out, thinking it would be full of ancient bottles containing some noxious sludge. But no. It was packed full with letters, invitations, bills and receipts, neatly entered in date order – between the years 1904 and 1907. The following chapters contain the story in the letters which we found.

All the letters in italics in the text are as written and unaltered.

The Carswell Sisters

Daughters of Councillor Morris Carswell,
J.P. of Murcia, Pollokshields, Glasgow

Jane   **Born 1862**
Married Thomas H Kirk, solicitor in Largs

Margaret Morris ('Meg')   **Born 1863**
Married T H Sandry, Lloyds Surveyor, Falmouth
Lived at Pendennis House

Eliza   **Born 1869**
Married

Helen   **Born 1872**
Married

Isabella ('Tibbie')   **Born 1874**
Married Henry Penlerick.
Emigrated to South Africa.

Emily ('Em' or 'Emma')   **Born 1876**

Susan Maud   **Born 1877**
Married

Catherine Octavia ('Katie')   **Born 1878**

Florence Nona   **Born 1879**
(Called the 'Wee Wife' by her sisters)
Married Bill McCall, who worked for Morris Carswell.
Lived at 8 Beaton Road, Maxwell , Park, Glasgow.

And two sons:

Alex	(1865 – 1872)
Morris	Born 1871

1
September
1904

James Hocking loved these early mornings, to be first in the shop to sort out the mail, to get ahead and develop the films that customers brought in, in increasing quantities during the season.

Today, in late September the sun was rising over the Roseland, the air clean and salty, ships at anchor in the Carrick Roads, little boats busy round the quays. Sometimes he would run to work down Jacob's Ladder, all 111 steps, but on this particular morning he came down the ope by the Polytechnic and into the street. Mr Oliver was hanging a bunch of rubber beach shoes outside his shop, rather optimistically, James thought. The water cart was already sprinkling the street. Four dray horses were pulled up by the Royal Hotel, their driver rolling barrels along the pavement and down the chute into the Royal's cellars.

He paused a moment, to gaze at the shop which was the hub of his life – The Strand Pharmacy, established 1818. Camera House – all painted boldly on the upper wall and F J Wilmer M.P.S. on the signboard over the five display windows.

Before unlocking the door, he checked the windows – time the toiletries display was changed. He'd see to that this morning; then he unlocked the door and picked up the early post on the mat. Before checking it, he paused behind the counter and took another letter from his pocket – a small neat envelope, addressed to him at home. It had been waiting for him beside the toast rack at breakfast time. This envelope had caused his mother considerable interest.

'There's a letter for you James,' she said. 'I've put it by your plate.'

'Thank you, mother. Good morning father.'

'Morning James.'

He drew up his chair and set about the bacon and eggs on the plate before him.

'The post mark's Glasgow,' his mother continued.

'Yes, I can see it is.'

His mother buttered her slice of toast and picked up the marmalade jar.

'And who do you know in Glasgow, may I ask?'

'You may ask, mother, but it could be one of half a dozen people. It's probably someone wanting their film to be developed.'

His mother chewed briskly.

'Really? I should have thought all your business letters would be addressed to the shop. I hope it's not the young lady you were seen with, walking along Castle Drive.'

'Now why should you hope that?'

'Because she's not suitable for you.'

'But she …'

'Don't bother to argue James. She's one of these flighty new century young women I see only too often these days. No commonsense – white dress, broderie anglaise, silly shoes – totally unsuitable for wear about the town. Goes to one of those Scotch churches, I shouldn't wonder – and certainly not a life companion for you.'

'Life companion?' James spluttered. 'I take a girl for a walk along Castle Drive and you infer from that I'm going to marry her? Really, mother, that is ridiculous.'

Mrs Hocking poured more tea for her husband.

'Don't call me ridiculous, James, for I am not. But you're going to make a name for yourself if you're constantly seen in her company. Why, Mrs Kitto said only yesterday ...'

'Oh, I see now, Mrs Kitto. That woman has eyes everywhere. Surely you know by now that you can't believe half of what she says?'

James was annoyed. He refused the toast proffered by his father.

'Mrs Kitto,' his mother said weightily, 'Mrs Kitto is a good friend of mine. Anyway, open the letter and tell us who's writing to you.'

Mr Hocking intervened.

'Now Ellen, you forget, James is a grown man. He doesn't have to explain to us who sends him correspondence.'

James picked up the letter and put it in his pocket.

'Thank you father,' he said. 'Well, I must be off.'

In the silence of the shop, he slit the envelope and took out the letter, glancing at the signature. As he had suspected, the sender was Miss Katie Carswell.

Dear Mr Hocking

I have always been expecting those photos which you promised me. Surely they are very fine to take such a time? I am afraid you must have a very bad opinion of me or are very lazy yourself. I read that you are having great heat in the sunny South just now, it must be a nice change for you folks! I am taking Pa away for the weekend today,

13

and my sister Emma went away ages ago, so I have just written to enquire if she intends returning for the Christmas festivities. You should have your holiday before the fair weather flies to Bonnie Scotland. I suppose you will be boating a lot if it's so hot – I trust your style has improved –

Yours v. sincerely
Katie O Carswell

'Trust your style has improved...' he read again. Absolutely typical of Katie, cheeky, provocative with a great sense of fun. They had taken his father's boat several times, from its mooring at Greenbank and had headed up the Penryn River and across to Flushing. The second time they had each brought their cameras and taken photographs. She had tied a muslin scarf over her extravagantly ruffled white hat to protect it from the sea breeze, her face beneath it vivid, interested in all she saw about her. They had moored at Flushing, and he had carried the picnic basket, provided by her sister Meg, and found a sheltered place beyond the village, taking photographs of each other and trying to capture the effects of the sun shadows on the water.

Two days later she had returned to her home in Glasgow and he had promised to develop her photos and send them on when they were ready. It was then that he realised that he didn't know her address. He had intended to walk along to Meg's house one evening, and ask her, but the last games of the tennis season, and evening duty opening had kept him busy.

He noticed with some amusement that she knew his address – had doubtless walked along Wodehouse Terrace to check up – how fortunate that his mother had not been gazing out of the parlour window between her cherished pot plants at the time.

The doorbell rang as the boy apprentice Harry came in.

'You've forgotten to open the side door Mr Hocking,' he said cheerfully, 'so I came in the posh way.'

'Fair enough,' James said, and turned to sort out the rest of the early delivery.

He slipped Katie's letter into his pocket and went up the winding staircase to the top of the building. Here he unlocked the door of the first attic room. Some months ago now, he had asked Mr Wilmer if he might use this room to answer correspondence, to read and so on. Mr Wilmer gave his consent willingly. James suspected that his employer knew of the constraints of living at home, the endless inquisitiveness of Mrs Hocking, the lack of privacy, the necessity of explaining his every hour of the day to her.

The attic was dark, with only a skylight to admit the sun. James had bought an old revolving chair in the auction room, and had made a comfortable seat by padding it with red cushions from the drapery in Market Street. A table, also from the auction room, had been hauled upstairs with the help of Harry. On it James had placed his blotter, pen tray and ink, and a paraffin lamp which was useful on dark evenings.

Because time was short this morning, he tucked Katie's letter under the blotter and ran downstairs to start the day's work, though before he began to make up the stock medicines, he went into his small dark room, where he developed the photographs. He found Katie's prints and packed them up. Harry would post it later in the morning. Then he took out an addressed sheet of the shop writing paper.

F J Wilmer, Dispensing Chemist, 8 Market Strand,
Falmouth

Dear Miss Carswell,

Thank you for your letter. I hope you will like
the photographs, especially the shot I took of you
at the oars catching crabs which I thought
particularly fetching. However, in future, would
you please direct any letter you care to send me to
the above address? This would avoid a number of
inconvenient questions at home – that is, if you
care to write to me again, as I hope you will.

I hope that when you come down again to visit
your sister and brother-in-law, I will be permitted
to help you improve your oarsmanship! Truly
though, I look forward to your next holiday in
sometimes sunny Falmouth.

Yours sincerely,
James Hocking.

Before he left for lunch – served at 1 p.m. sharp as Mrs
Hocking decreed – he found an empty wooden Elliman's
Embrocation box and took it up to the attic, and placed
Katie's letter in it. He hauled out the table and stowed
the box safely in the cupboard behind it.

During the winter of 1904-05, several letters and
invitations were added to the box, as Falmouth bade
farewell to all its visitors and life could resume its usual
placid programme of homely winter events.

*Mr and Mrs Downing Pascoe request the pleasure
of Mr J Hocking's company on the evening of
Friday 18th inst. At 7.30 o'clock. 49 Market Street
Falmouth. Whist and Music.*

But before that, on the 9th September James had gone to
Newquay on his half day, to Hurcombe the Jewellers for
an important purchase, the receipt for which went into
the box. 'William E. Hurcomb. Jeweller Watchmaker
and Silversmith' runs the decorative receipt heading.

*Mr J. Hocking : To gold keyless English lever
hunter watch by Grimshaw and Baxter London
No47374 £13-10-0.*

Over the penny stamp is written, *'Received 9.9.04. Wm
E Hurcomb, Wm. Sykes.'*
   This was something he had been saving for – his first
indulgence since passing his pharmaceutical
examinations in London three years ago.

Then, another invitation:

Observatory, Falmouth, Dec 8th

*Dear Mr Hocking, I am having a few friends here
for a game of progressive whist on Tuesday next at
8 o'clock. May we have the pleasure of your
company? We are strangers to Mr Turvey, but if
he will accept an invitation from Mother, we shall
be very pleased to see him. Will you be good
enough to ask him for her?*

17

Sincerely yours,
C. Donald Kitto.

P.S.   If you do not care for whist, there will be others not playing.   Please bring some music.

Evenings at the Observatory were always enjoyable – the whist stopping for an interval to make time for a splendid table, decorated with flowers, which was piled high with tiny pastries, sandwiches, pork pies, and to top it all, a magnificent confection of chocolate éclairs, cream filled. Perhaps it was no wonder that James was prone to indigestion, having already eaten lunch and a high tea at home.

Turvey was a family friend, staying for a week or so, known to them all as Topsy.   James gave him the invitation, and planned to forget his music. It would make a pleasant change not to have to perform. There had been little time for practice recently, and he dreaded giving anything other than his best at these evenings. He knew very well that the audience would consist of his friends and his many acquaintances, but that was even worse in some ways, letting himself down and becoming the victim of consolatory remarks was far worse than honest criticism.

1905

2
May 1905

Winter passed and he welcomed the first Lenten lilies, the primroses and violets growing in the hedges of the sheltered lanes that he liked to walk on Sunday afternoons, and, as the evenings became lighter, sometimes after work.

One May morning his Market Strand post was brightened by a colourful post card from Las Palmas. He and Katie had corresponded occasionally during the winter and he had felt a little envious of her news that her father was taking members of his family to Las Palmas. They were staying at the Metropol Hotel, a large multi windowed building with balconies on all four floors, which looked out over a halcyon sea. Katie's message took up most of the blue sky and a cramped four lines below the photograph.

19 May 1905. We expect to arrive home by the first and are trying to have from 28th [April] in London to see the shops. We sail on the Orion – hope it's a decent boat. Later – our boat is in before its time and so we leave here this morning, and are having a day or two in London. Weather simply lovely. If you wrote I won't get it – have missed all home letters. None of us were seasick. KOC.

After the clear air and blue sea of Las Palmas, London was airless and dusty, the streets dirty and the noise of the traffic louder even than Glasgow. Within an hour of leaving their hotel, Katie and her sister Emma felt hot and grimy. Bond Street had proved disappointing.

'Och, we can find better shops in Glasgow any day,' said Katie and Emma had to agree.

Liberty's though was a different matter. They were tempted through its doors by the glimpse of yards of silk of every hue, and rich velvets draped over screens and tables.

Once inside, each department led them deeper into the shop

'Em, have you noticed the assistants?'

Emma looked; the women assistants were not clothed in the usual black uniform, but in velvet cut on mediaeval lines which flowed gracefully to the floor; their long sleeves, wide at the wrist, were edged with contrasting silk. They were not constrained by corsetry either, the bones of which ensured a slim waist. Instead the gowns skimmed their bodies in easy tucks and folds. They looked cool and comfortable.

'They almost make a convert of me to the free-flowing look – imagine that smocking instead of corsets,' Emma said.

'I think I'll not bother while my waist is twenty two inches. Time enough when I'm a middle aged matron for all that drapery.'

'You a matron? That's hard to imagine.'

'All the same,' said Katie, gazing at a dress modelled on a plaster figure, 'there's a lot to be said for the new twentieth century style.'

They pored over cabinets of jewellery, fashioned from silver and pewter, admired the curving lines and the depths of colour in the enamels and stones.

'Not a diamond or sapphire to be seen,' said Emma, 'Just polished stones that we could pick up on the beach.'

Katie didn't reply. She was gazing at a silver buckle, inset with amethyst flowers and green enamel leaves.

Scarves and shawls were swathed on wooden stands. They passed them and went downstairs to the Japanese rooms, and were taken aback by the contrast in furniture and pottery so different from what they were used to seeing. The spare and delicate pictures too, were very different from the ponderous Stag at Bay which hung in the hall at home.

'I'm going to treat myself,' said Emma as they went upstairs again, 'I'm going to buy that lovely Indian shawl. It'll keep out the draughts next winter.'

'You've made up my mind for me,' Katie said, and while Emma was buying her shawl, she returned to the jewellery room and bought the silver buckle.

And now she was planning her next visit to Falmouth. She had fixed dates with Meg who was always happy to see her – indeed see anyone from home. T.H. had looked at her somewhat quizzically the last time she was down, but Meg must have done some behind-the-scenes explaining the reason for her little sister's devotion to Falmouth which was so great that she was coming down two or three times this year. The pull, of course, was the young pharmacist at Wilmer's.

Getting away could be a problem too. Pa was such a fuss pot. It was neither seemly nor safe for a young girl (for although she was twenty three, to Pa she was always a child) to be travelling alone and crossing London to Paddington – a journey he believed to be fraught with danger. Fortunately Pa had no objections about Falmouth in June and Katie was able to get away with

23

the minimum of explanations as to why she wanted to visit Meg again so soon, instead of going to stay with one of her other married sisters.

Pa approved of her visits to Meg who was the second oldest of the girls, sixteen years older than Katie. He looked on his older daughters as an excellent influence on the younger children (there were nine girls), for they had done much to bring up the younger ones ever since the grievous death of their mother after baby Florence (Nona) was born. Each of the older girls had a special favourite amongst the younger children, and Meg was particularly fond of Katie.

Katie on church steps in Falmouth, 1905
Photo Taken by James

James had suggested that she leave her holiday till later. After all, she'd had her Las Palmas holiday, but time was flying by, and she knew Pa would never understand her wanting to go away just as winter was setting in – Falmouth, he'd say was for the summer.

So she packed her bags and set off in the middle of June, taking the afternoon 'tea' train from Glasgow to London. Pa didn't like her to leave Glasgow on the night train. There'd be far less risk of upsetting him if she departed in the afternoon.

Another thing, she asked T.H. (her brother-in-law) to sort out the night train from Paddington, which travelled right through to Falmouth, so that she didn't have to change at Truro. She'd had to do that once and it was really quite nerve wracking, finding a porter to haul her trunk and bags off the Penzance-bound train, and hastily load them onto the branch line to Falmouth.

The last bit of the journey took half an hour, and she loved these early morning arrivals. She had learned every tunnel, viaduct and station of those twelve miles. There were the green fields and steep little hills, the long tunnel soon after they left Truro and the precipitous viaduct at Carnon before the halt at Perranwell. From here on she began to look for glimpses of the Fal. The few minutes at Penryn seemed to last forever, and then – there was the Penryn Creek widening on the left, boats busy about their morning work, and then the run down to Falmouth Station.

Usually T.H. met her, taking charge of her luggage and arranging for a porter to carry it to Pendennis House. Meg would be at the door to greet her, plump, smiling and unfashionably golden in the warm sun.

The house smelt of beeswax and soap, on Fridays overlaid by the glorious scent of pasties cooking in the oven.

'As I've married a Cornishman,' Meg had said, 'I must learn how to make a proper Cornish pasty.' She had soon found a friend who offered to teach her, so her pasties were filled with the right amounts of beef and potatoes, and the pastry was unexceptionable.

She usually gave Katie the bedroom, above the dining room. It was light and pretty; Katie would run up the stairs, fling off her coat and hat, and wash her face and hands in the soft Cornish water.

3
June 1905

And now Katie was here, in 'her' bedroom at Pendennis House, the journey over. Her luggage was stacked on the rack at the end of the bed, and since her last visit T.H. and Meg had installed wash basins in all the bedrooms with running hot and cold water – a great innovation. She surveyed the pink roses on the new wallpaper, and the embroidered pink counterpane on her bed with approval. It was typical of Meg, who took great pleasure in making the house comfortable and inviting. But most of all, it was so good to be with Meg again – Meg who understood her so well – sometimes too well.

A glance in the mirror showed her the extent of the smuts which she had acquired on the journey – her white gloves were blackened. Her face and the high collar of her blouse had not escaped either. She felt hot and travel weary. She took off the blouse, and washed in the soft, warm water. Then she unpinned her hair and brushed it until her scalp tingled. The lunch gong rang, so she found a clean blouse – fortunately she had packed them at the top of the trunk so they were not too creased, tied her hair back, and ran down the stairs to lunch.

The pasty was hot and delicious, bursting with meat and gravy, and she was very hungry.

'I do believe your pasties are getting even better,' she remarked to Meg, her fork tracing the neat crimping that sealed the pastry.

'Yes,' said T.H., 'they're very good, my dear. I think we could say your apprentice days of pasty making are over, and now you're a fully qualified pasty artisan'.

27

'Oh good,' Meg said. 'My only regret is that I haven't a certificate to show for my efforts. Think how smart it would look, framed and hanging above the sideboard.'

Early strawberries from the garden followed, topped with clotted cream.

'What would you like to do this afternoon, Katie? Unfortunately it's my day for the child welfare clinic – I weigh the babies you know. You can come with me if you like, or maybe you would like to rest? I don't suppose you slept too well on the train.'

'I think I'll go and look at the sea first. Then I might walk into town to buy some film.'

'H'm,' said T.H., 'I don't want to put you off Katie, but just look at the clouds building up, from the south west too.'

Sure enough, the sunshine had disappeared, the room suddenly looked cold and bleak, even the heavy velvet curtains were flapping in the rising wind. There would be no pleasant stroll into town.

'I think I'll leave the town till the morning then.' Katie said. 'But I'll go and look at the sea, then I'll unpack.'

'Well, don't get blown away.'

Even in the rain, Gyllingvase beach was glorious. The wide sweep of sand was deserted, the tide rising. She stood on the road, watching the slanting rain on the pewter grey water, and then ran down onto the beach. Rain drops pitted the sand and the wind tugged at the shawl with which she had covered her hair and tied under her chin. She breathed deeply, revelling in the clean air after the hours on the train. She walked along the beach ignoring the wavelets that frothed and foamed round her feet, the wind from the sea blowing hard against her, then turned and ran with the wind at her back, along the sands and up onto the road again.

She was relieved to find that Meg was still out when she returned to the house – she could imagine her horror, at the sight of this storm wracked creature that her mirror showed when she reached her bedroom. She stripped off her shoes and stockings. The hems of her skirt and petticoat were soaked. She found her wrapper in the trunk and whisked the wet clothes down to the kitchen. Here Maud, Meg's maid, put them to dry in front of the range, with many exclamations of dismay.

'Shall I put the kettle on miss?' she asked. 'It's a warm drink you'll be wanting.'

'Oh, Maud, yes please. But I must go and change and unpack.'

Ten minutes later, as she pulled on her old house skirt, Maud arrived with a tray of tea and two cups and saucers.

'Mrs Sandry'll be in soon, miss, and knowing her, she'll probably want her tea up here with you.'

Meg appeared as Katie drank her first cup and was opening her trunk to unpack her clothes. Meg subsided onto the bed and poured her tea.

'Well, what new from home?' she asked.

'Oh, I've so much to tell you. We had a lovely time on the cruise. I'd like to go back to Las Palmas one day, but I've just walked along Gyllingvase Beach and really there's nothing to compare with Cornwall.'

'And Pa? Did he enjoy it?'

'Yes. You know what fun he is on holiday – we took carriages every day to look at the sights and countryside, and after dinner we walked in the sunset, along the beach. Then Pa would join his old cronies for bridge and whisky and was still playing until the early hours.

It's sweet of him to take us, I'm sure he enjoys himself as much as Em and Nona and me.'

'How's Winkie?'

Katie thought for a moment about her friend before replying.

'Well, poor Winkie. Em and I are quite worried about her. Her dear father-in-law Paterson has written to tell them he's marrying again, in September. He's nearly eighty and apparently his intended is only thirty. You know he gives a third of his income to charity every year? Well it seems this young person is also interested in his missionary work, and as it turns out, in the missionary himself.'

'Silly old man – eighty did you say?'

'I did. And to make matters worse he's going off with her to live in Edinburgh. He's left his Glasgow house to his eldest son, who's married, and a very good sort; but his daughter and her sister will have a much harder time of it. His son isn't going to live in the house, but let Mary and Jane stay there … we think at home that they'll have to count the pennies, because of course he looked after all the household expenses.'

'However will they manage then?'

'They have their own money inherited from their mother's side of the family, but that will have to go much farther than when their pa was at home.'

'The moral of this sad tale seems to be "Never trust a missionary."

'True. And, of course, Winkie being married to the second son means that they are more or less unaffected by it all.'

'Though presumably,' Meg said watching Katie hang her blouses and skirts in the wardrobe, 'When the old man dies his young wife will inherit his remaining worldly wealth, rather than his sons.'

'Exactly.'

Chattering together, they emptied the trunk and the bags of the multitude of clothes and shoes that Katie deemed necessary for a month in Falmouth. As she unpacked she felt a shiver of joyful anticipation inside her, for tomorrow morning straight after breakfast, she would hurry down the town and surprise James when she entered the shop. In the meantime, here was her dear Meg, so delighted to see her.

'Oh, did I tell you?' she said. 'When we were in London I bought some beautiful white self-striped sateen, and Mrs McPhie is making it up for me and sending it on. And this is the buckle I bought in Liberty's to sew on the belt, when it arrives.'

Meg took the buckle and examined it. 'How lovely,' she said, 'and very modern.'

'I know. Em and I looked at the Liberty dress styles, all flowing velvet and smocking and easy sleeves, not a sign of any bones or corsets or underpinnings. They looked so comfortable – some day I might have one, just to try.'

'I'm very tempted,' Meg said. 'Somehow fastening my corset gets harder and harder.'

There was a discreet tap at the door, and T.H.'s head appeared.

'I don't like to interrupt you girls, but are we to have any supper this evening?'

'What, you're back already? Did you leave early?'

Meg glanced at the bedside clock, and jumped up.

'Good heavens, is that the time?'

She hurried down the stairs.

The sun woke Katie next morning, for she had opened the heavy chintz curtains before climbing into bed, leaving the muslin ones in place; through them the light

31

was misty. She pulled back the muslin, and regarded the day. The garden looked fresh and twinkled with drops of yesterday's rain. Again she felt amazed at the way the weather could change in Cornwall – yesterday howling wind and heavy rain, today, already the sun was warm and a light breeze stirred the trees and ruffled the water in the harbour. After breakfast she told Meg that she was going into town.

'Is there anything you need?' she asked.

'I don't think so, though if you're going into the chemist's you could buy two bars of that nice Cusson's soap.'

'In that case,' said T.H. 'you could take my last film in to be developed.'

Katie ran upstairs and selected her prettiest hat, a cartwheel confection topped by white ribbon and lace which she arranged at the fashionable angle which needed severe pinning into place. She adjusted the belt of her shirt waister, found T.H.'s film and a basket and set off. Her pace quickened, as she reached Arwenack Street, though she paused to glance at the tantalising views of the harbour from the Custom House and the Fish Strand Quays.

She paused for a moment to look into a jeweller's window, to check her hat. It would never do to arrive at Market Strand looking flushed and hurried. Then at a more sedate pace she came to the curved frontage of the chemist's shop.

James was standing at his favourite lookout post, the centre window of the five that curved round the corner of Market Strand. From here he had a grandstand view of Market Street, always busy, as well as all the traffic to and from High Street. Across the road was the hotel, and the quay which was in the process of being extended, causing an immense amount of dust from the stone work, in addition to the noise of the builders and of the large carts delivering the granite, metal and timber which were needed for the quay's construction.

He had been the junior pharmacist in Mr Wilmer's shop now for three years. He often reflected on how fortunate he had been to be offered the position as soon as he had qualified. Mr Wilmer, a genial and busy man, was beginning to want a little more spare time and a little less dispensing, and the appointment of James gave him more leisure.

Today, the sun was shining, drying the pavements from yesterday's downpour, and the boats were bobbing in the harbour beyond the quay. The shop had been very busy from nine o'clock, but now, at eleven, customers had eased off and he had a few minutes to spare. Katie had written earlier in the week to say that she intended to arrive on Friday. He had hoped she might come into town in the afternoon, but he couldn't blame her if the torrential rain and gale had put her off.

And here she was: a slender girl, with a trim waist, walking quickly towards him, along the pavement. He noticed she was wearing one of her wide brimmed hats at a rakish and no doubt highly fashionable angle, before he went to open the door for her.

'Good morning, Miss Carswell. It's very good to see you.'

'Good morning to you too, Mr Hocking, though my name is Katie, remember? As you see, I've arrived according to plan.'

She placed her basket on one of the chairs beside the counter.

'Well done, Katie. I hoped you'd come in this morning.'

'Of course – as soon as I could. Thank goodness you didn't see me yesterday afternoon though. I went for a peep at the sea at Gyllingvase, and returned to Meg's looking like a drowned rat.'

'Silly girl,' Jamie said. 'The sea'll be there whatever the weather. I hope you didn't catch cold.'

'Not a bit of it. Oh James, it's so good to be here again. I've got the photographs, but even so I began to forget what you look like.'

'I know. It's been a long, long time. But I'll spend every possible moment with you while you're here.'

They gazed at each other, oblivious of the curious glances of the other customers, until James felt a sharp prod in his ribs as Miss Hawke, the somewhat severe lady assistant, passed behind him on her way to the dispensary. He jumped and returned to the present.

'Is there anything I can get for you Katie?'

'Yes indeed. I've a film here that my brother-in-law would like you to develop. And I'd like two rolls of film for my own camera, if you please. I forgot to buy any before I left home.'

'These will be for your Kodak?'

'No. Oh James. Such fun. Pa gave me a beautiful new camera for my birthday. It's a Lizar's of Glasgow, one of the new folding ones. Look, I've brought it with me. What do you think?'

She put the camera on the counter.

'I think you're looking prettier than ever.'

'Oh really – you're making me blush – I mean, what abut the camera?'

'My word,' said James lifting it gently from the counter.

'It's their very latest, isn't it?'

Together they admired the camera's modern improvements, the leather bellows, and the trim case.

'Well, I envy you,' James said at last. 'I'm afraid I'm still jogging along with my old Kodak, though I'm considering getting their Number Four, Screen Focus. I can use it with roll film or with plates.'

They talked amicably together, while other customers came in, to be served by Mr Wilmer or Miss Hawke.

'Would you like to come for a walk – say tomorrow afternoon, if it's fine?' James asked, conscious of Miss Hawke's beady eye fixed upon him, as she attended to yet another customer.

'Rain or fine,' said Katie, 'Come along about half past two.'

Fortunately the days that followed were fine and sunny. Two schooners and an elegant barquentine rested in the harbour, rocking gently on the calm water. Katie would stay for minutes at a time absorbing their beauty of line, not bothering with her camera, but imprinting the scene on her mind. James took several photographs, planning to send them to her when her memories of Falmouth became indistinct over the long winter to come.

They walked everywhere – in the evenings along Castle Drive, pausing to sit on the seats along the way, happy in the warmth of the dusk and the deep blue of the sea, talking, kissing, his arm enfolding her shoulders.

They talked about everything – their thoughts and feelings that could not be written in their letters to one another. They met at every possible time that James was not working, usually in the evenings. James would hurry home for a change of clothes (Katie complained that his working suit smelt like the dispensary) and meet her to walk to Swanpool, Gyllingvase, or along Greenbank.

One evening they found a secluded seat off the path in Kimberley Park. Standard roses scented the still air and forget-me-nots shimmered blue beneath them.

35

Kimberley Park Gardens 1905
Photo taken by James

'Tell me,' said Katie. 'Now and then you mention your time in London, but why, exactly, were you there?

James was surprised, surely she knew?

'I was there for six months altogether, putting in the theory study that is necessary before the finals of the Society's examinations. I was part time at the School of Pharmacy. I spent the rest in reading the recommended tomes. We would break out sometimes though and we would go up to the West End, see a show and eat well at one of the small restaurants and steak houses that are everywhere. Then early in the morning we would roll back to our digs, thankful that it was Sunday.'

'But you don't mean to tell me that pharmacists only train for six months?'

'No, no. First you have to serve a long apprenticeship with a qualified man. I was lucky. Mr Wilmer took me on and he really was an excellent boss. He taught me a tremendous amount. And of course during that time I lived at home.'

'That was easy for you – no digs to find.'

'In some ways, yes. But it was also frustrating, especially when my brother Ed went off to train as an engineer. I envied him that – seeing the world.'

'But you made up for it by going to London.'

He smiled.

'Yes, I'm afraid the candles were burned at both ends quite a bit. It was a good place to be, my digs with Mr and Mrs Pearce. He was born in Cornwall, you see, and my parents knew him, so it was all easily arranged, and other pharmacy students were there too.'

'So what happened when you burned both ends of the candle?'

'Nothing much. We'd come back to the Pearces and drink sarsaparilla and dandelion and burdock …'

'No beer? No whisky?'

'Sadly no. We were all Methodists of one sort or another, so we couldn't fuel our fun with alcohol.'

'How dull.'

'Not at all. We smoked our pipes and had long philosophical conversations, and talked about our ambitions and were duly sorrowful about the old Queen's death. We even joined the crowd to watch the funeral procession.'

'Well, she'd certainly been Queen for a long time, hadn't she? I remember Pa saying she became Queen when he was an infant, and he was sixty five when she died.'

'So he's sixty eight now. Does he plan to retire?'

'Not really. He goes down to the office every morning at eight o'clock, wet or fine, light or dark. But he keeps shorter hours these days. But what about your father? I'd like to meet him, and your mother. I'm sure she's not as difficult as you make her out to be.'

'Usually not. But she is apt to take on points of view from which she won't move, especially when it concerns one of the family. One of her cousins, for instance, became an actress. Mother was horrified, and although the lady has been married for many years to a perfectly respectable grocer with his own business, she remains adamant that the cousin is a loose woman. When we were younger, we weren't allowed to visit her, presumably because of the evil influence she would have over our young, innocent minds.'

Katie chuckled.

'I'd really like to meet them though,' she said. 'It seems the open thing to do; after all, we've nothing to hide. Who knows, they might even find me quite unlike their earlier impressions.'

She turned towards him, and as he took her hand and leaned to kiss her, Katie knew that she was not imagining the love that was in his eyes. It was reassuring.

But the Hockings' attitude towards her continued to concern her. That evening, as she brushed her hair, she wondered why they kept their distance. If only she could meet them, surely they would find that she was just a younger edition of Meg – and she knew that Meg was on cordial terms with them. And as for herself, she only wished to continue on good terms with James and his relations and friends. After all, she was not some undesirable young woman to whom their son had taken a fancy. She was a Carswell of Glasgow.

James also was well aware that he must introduce Katie to his parents. That same evening, he asked his mother if he might bring Katie to tea next Sunday.

'Sunday?'

'Yes. We hope to go for a walk on Sunday afternoon, and I thought I might invite her here for a cup of tea.'

Mrs Hocking considered this proposal. He knew by her expression that she was searching for some obstacle to his plan and his heart sank as he waited.

'This Sunday won't be convenient. We have already invited Mr and Mrs Lamb for afternoon tea and we shall be discussing church affairs.'

'Very well. Perhaps next Sunday then?'

'Perhaps. We shall see.'

In fact, the meeting came about before any of them expected, and it was a memory that was to haunt James for many years. It became the kind of memory that surfaces on sleepless nights, or when he was alone in the dispensary, his chest contracting till he could hardly breathe.

It was after Sunday morning service, at the local chapel door. The minister was chatting to members of his congregation, in those moments when devout silence and attention were replaced by a cheerful bonhomie, and the minister jolly, having successfully negotiated his sermon.

The Hockings stopped for a few polite words with him, Mrs Hocking in black bombazine, discreetly hatted, and her husband, eighty four now, dignified, portly, leaning on his silver handled cane.

Waiting for them to move on, James saw Katie, with her sister Meg and T.H. They had paused to speak to friends. Katie's crisp grey and white striped poplin

39

dress, her lacy grey hat that appeared to be the nest for a flock of grey and pink birds, captured all eyes, - significantly, those of Mrs Hocking.

Then Meg, who James knew was aware of his and Katie's growing affection, stepped forward to introduce her to Mrs Hocking.

'Good morning, Mrs Hocking. I don't think you have met my younger sister Katie? Mr and Mrs Hocking – Katie Carswell.

Mrs Hocking drew herself to her full height.

'So you are the young woman I've heard about,' she said.

'How do you do,' replied Katie, smiling. 'I hope you've only heard good about me?'

She quailed before the older woman's cold, prominent eyes.

'What I have heard about you is nothing to the purpose,' Mrs Hocking began unpromisingly. 'It's what I've seen of you – careering around the streets in those silly shoes at all hours of the clock. I should have thought your mother could have taught you better.'

Katie had held out her hand to take Mrs Hocking's, if proffered, but now she dropped it to her side. For a few moments she was utterly at a loss.

James was about to step forward to intervene, but Meg was before him.

'Time we must go Katie,' she interposed. 'Sunday lunch will not roast all by itself.'

Katie turned at her sister's hand on her arm, but she was indignant. How dare any outsider criticise her and her family – someone who knew so little of them, too? She faced Mrs Hocking, and James' heart sank to see the steely look in her eyes.

'Unfortunately, Mrs Hocking, my mother died and so I was brought up mainly by Meg and my other older

40

sisters. They have all done their best for us younger ones, and if my choice of dress does not please you, then the fault is mine, and no one else's.'

There was a silence around them. Other groups nearby became aware of something amiss, and glanced curiously at the two women.

Having taken in the full implication of Katie's words, Mrs Hocking regained her self possession.

'Well really, Miss Carswell, I have rarely heard such barefaced impertinence towards an older woman. You have much to teach her, Mrs Sandry.'

Meg looked startled at this sideways swipe.

'Come Katie,' she said, and they turned away.

'That was unwise, Katie,' Meg remarked as they walked home. 'She is a good lady, but not one to be crossed.'

Katie's cheeks were burning and her eyes stung as she tried to hold back angry tears.

'I couldn't stop myself. I was perfectly pleasant until she insulted me, you Meg, why, our whole family. And I was not going to stand there and listen meekly to what she had to say.'

'I know,' said Meg. 'It's very hard, but if you want to remain friends with James you'll have to learn to hold your tongue.'

They walked home through the town thus avoiding the road which the Hockings always took. The day was sunny with a light sea breeze that cooled Katie's cheeks. Small boats rocked gently in the harbour, but today she didn't stop to look down to the quays, as she usually did. She felt the tears choking her throat, and could take no part in Meg's and T.H.'s bland conversation.

Reaching the house at last, they entered the cool dim hall. Tall delphiniums in a green vase were lit by the landing window above. Meg disappeared towards the

41

kitchen, still wearing her hat and gloves, and murmuring something about the vegetables. There was a promising smell of roasting meat as she opened the kitchen door.

T.H. turned to Katie as she stumbled towards the stairs.

'Don't be upset, Katie,' he said gently. 'It's a storm in a tea cup, you'll see. It'll soon blow over.'

'But James ...'

'If James cares anything about you, this will make no difference to his feelings.'

She looked up into his kind blue eyes.

'Meg is lucky,' she said, and ran up the stairs to her room.

She flung off her hat, scattering hat pins all over the carpet and tugged off her gloves which clung to her hot damp fingers. Why, oh why, couldn't she control her temper? It spoiled everything. Even Pa had told her that she must learn to keep her feelings to herself Certainly Mrs Hocking had so unfairly attacked her, but how much better it would have been if she had just continued to smile at her. By answering back she had descended to the other woman's level.

She sank onto the bed and wept. Gone now was any hope that James would continue their friendship, for he had great regard for his parents, as she knew. She remembered how during last winter and spring she had thought about him continually, had come to imagine that perhaps ... and she had destroyed all this with a couple of hasty sentences.

This afternoon they had planned a longer walk. He had been due to call for her at half past two, as usual on a Sunday, and they were to go to Maenporth, have tea at a cottage there and return by the cliff path. Now she knew he wouldn't be coming.

She ran cold water into the washbasin and splashed her hot face and neck. The gong sounded in the hall. Lunch was ready. She dried her face, took the remaining pins from her hair, brushed it and hastily wove it into one heavy chestnut plait. She found a clean handkerchief and went down to the dining room.

No one commented on her red and puffy eyelids. Despite having felt that she couldn't possibly eat any lunch, she found that when the plate of roast lamb, new peas and potatoes was put before her, she was extremely hungry.

'Did you say you were going for a walk this afternoon?' Meg asked as they finished with strawberries and thick clotted cream.

'I was,' Katie said, 'But after this morning, I don't expect to see James again.'

'Oh, come now Katie, surely …?'

'No. I'm afraid I've burned my boats! You didn't see his expression. I did! I think I'd better write some overdue letters and catch up with my mending.'

She helped Meg with washing the dishes, for Maud had Sunday afternoon and evening off. Having washed the pans and cooking utensils, Maud always hurried along to her sister's house, to have her lunch with them.

'Very well,' Meg said. 'Don't forget that we're having a few friends in for supper this evening.'

Katie ran upstairs to fetch her pen, and then settled herself at the desk in the drawing room. This was placed in a bay window that overlooked the garden, a position detrimental to concentration on letters and bills, for Meg was very proud of her garden and now everything seemed to be in full bloom. Delphiniums grew in the border against the hedge, vying with sunflowers and hollyhocks for height. Before them grew a profusion of

43

aquilegias, larkspur, lilies and roses. Edging the lawn were pansies and primulas.

She gazed at the scene for a few moments, and then reluctantly settled to writing to Emma and Pa. She usually wrote to them weekly when she was away, but this holiday she had been remiss. They would be wondering if all was well with her.

She had just written: "Dear Pa and Em," on the Pendennis House writing paper when she heard the bell of the front door. Knowing that Meg was busy preparing a salad for this evening and T.H. had retired to his study with the Sunday newspaper, she put down her pen and went to answer it.

And there, on the doorstep, stood James.

'Oh,' Katie said, 'It's you.'

'It is indeed. Are you ready for our walk or had you forgotten?'

'I thought – well, I thought that after this morning you wouldn't be wanting to see me.'

'After this morning, I especially wanted to see you, Katie. May I come in? I'd rather not stand on the doorstep to talk to you.'

She opened the door more widely and he entered, closing it behind him. They stood together in the dimly lit hall.

'You look different,' he said. 'I know why, you've plaited your hair like a school girl. You look – adorable.'

'I must go and put it up. I really didn't think you'd be coming'.

'Well, I'm here. And it's for me to apologise for the behaviour of my mother. Granted she didn't know that your mother had died, but her words were vindictive, and I feel ashamed that you should have been treated like that by her.'

'But I was just as rude to her.'

'No you weren't. You were responding to her words, which in my view were unforgiveable. I have spoken to her about it, and she has admitted that she went too far. As for father, he was horrified.'

'I see.'

'So are we going for our walk, or would you rather not?'

'Oh James, please come in and wait for five minutes, and I'll be ready.'

'Don't bother to put up your hair again. It is lovely in its plait.'

She ran down the kitchen corridor to tell Meg the news.

'Have a lovely walk,' said Meg, carefully cutting radishes into rosettes. 'If James would like to come to supper, tell him he'll be very welcome.'

They set out along Castle Drive, the sea, blue under the sun, was at high tide; the beach and the Drive itself were deserted, drowsing in the heat. The hotel and the solid comfortable houses on their right seemed wrapped in the same after-Sunday-lunch somnolence as their owners.

At first they didn't speak very much, until they left the seaside and took the lane towards Swanpool. Here they settled on one of the wooden seats for a while.

'I'm glad I borrowed Meg's panama,' Katie remarked. 'The sun's getting hotter all the time. I must get one of my own, though a bit more up-to-date than this old thing.'

They watched the swans in silence. Each bird floated up to them in turn and then paddled away in disgust when no bread was forthcoming.

'I'm really sorry about this morning.' James said abruptly. 'I think my mother was taken by surprise when Meg introduced you.'

'Och, it's I who am to blame. Everyone's always warning me to rein in my temper, but as you heard, I'm not very good at it yet.'

'All the same, mother was quite out of order, and I can only apologise again for her. You must have been very upset. Father's rather deaf, you know, so he missed most of what was said. But he knew something was up, for when he got home, he asked me about it. "Pretty little maid, young Katie," he said. Mother nearly exploded with indignation.'

'But why? After all, I was perfectly civil to her to begin with.'

'I know. I'm afraid she must have been listening to gossip, and of course she always wears her buttoned boots around the town because of the cobblestones and uneven pavements.'

'Well, I really can't imagine why my shoes should be a subject of gossip. Ladies in Falmouth must be very short of things to talk about.'

He turned to her.

'I do sincerely hope this is not going to make any difference to our friendship, Katie. I'm sure she'll come round when she gets to know you better.'

He looked at her closely.

'Your eyes are a bit pink. You haven't been crying, have you?'

She looked up at him.

'Well yes. Meg said something when we were walking away, and it made me realise how stupid it was to annoy your mother – and then, you see, I thought I'd lost you forever.'

'Oh Katie, you should know me better than that. I shall forget about it, and you must too.'

They sat hand in hand until Katie jumped up, pulling him to his feet.

'Did you promise me tea this afternoon? I must have cried myself dry at lunch time, for I'm exceedingly thirsty now.'

'Right. On we go.'

They had tea at a little cottage beside the lane, its small garden brim-full with flowers and plants. Young lettuces competed with poppies and Canterbury bells and a clematis had woven its way along the fence and was clambering into an old apple tree. Sweet peas grew up an old ladder propped against the wall, and roses formed an archway over the porch. A small table and two wooden chairs stood hospitably on the small patch of lawn. There they were served tea in a brown teapot, and a newly baked Madeira cake.

They talked about their families, with all their peculiarities of speech and laughed at the stories of several eccentric great aunts with their whiskery chins, whom they dreaded having to kiss when they were children.

They wandered back to Pendennis House as the day began to cool and the sun dipped to cast great swathes of gold across the waves.

'Meg suggested that you might like to come home to supper with us,' Katie said. 'Would you like to? Have you time?'

'I should like to very much. I'll just go home to tell mother I shan't be in.'

'Really? Do you have to?'

James considered the ham sandwiches that would await him at home prepared the night before and doubtless already curling at the edges. He rarely ate them anyway.

'No.' he said, and then with more certainty, 'No, of course I don't.'

He felt pleased with his decision. It was a small step towards independence.

4

Supper was a cheerful affair, presided over by T H and Meg. There were two other couples there, Henry and Blanche Lawrence and the Everetts. Meg had produced an informal meal – cold gammon joint, salads, bread, cheeses and one of her famous Scottish raspberry trifles. Conversation was friendly, ranging over happenings in Falmouth, particularly including the final touches to the Prince of Wales pier.

The Prince himself with Princess Mary had laid the foundation stone two years ago, in a grand ceremony, and four weeks ago, on another great occasion, the Earl of Kimberley had declared the newly extended pier open. The improvements were impressive and everyone at supper had walked along the new length, and admired the extra width as well, for its easing of passenger crowding. Ferry boats were now able to arrive and depart without a scramble for a place at the quayside.

All this led on, as conversations will, to the state of the grass on the tennis courts, now lacking rain and turning browner by the day, and so by various byways to the question of votes for women. This was scorned by the men, who all agreed that the little woman was born to keep a happy household, adding to its number regularly and being a submissive and supportive wife and mother. That was when Katie, who had been listening to this patronising conversation for some minutes, finally spoke. James was startled by her eloquence and vehemence.

'Men have everything their own way,' she began. 'The world is designed entirely for their comfort and convenience. Why, we're raising funds in Glasgow for a

49

hostel for young university women. Of course, the men have had their halls of residence for years.'

There was a startled silence, until Mr Everett sought to assuage the storm.

'But Miss Carswell,' he began. 'Up until very recent years there has been no need to build women's halls of residence, for there have been no women students to fill them, so therefore there has been no problem as to where they should live.'

'Exactly,' Katie said. 'Universities were strictly men only. They still are, in the main. And in some, the women who have taken courses successfully have still not been eligible to receive the award of a degree.'

'But my dear,' interposed Henry Lawrence, 'many courses are entirely unsuited to women – take medical studies for instance. How utterly degrading they are for ladies, completely destroying their delicacy of mind and innocent femininity.'

'Och, bosh,' said Katie rudely. 'Women make excellent nurses and good doctors – the few that are practising – and do consider, Mr Lawrence, many women would prefer to consult a woman doctor.

'But it's not only the medical professions. There are so many doors closed to women because of their lack of education.'

'Well, well, well,' said Mr Lawrence jovially, turning to James, 'we seem to have quite a little firebrand here…'

'Don't tell me you're one of the dreaded bluestockings Miss Carswell,' said Mr Everett. 'Have you a yearning to go to University?'

Katie laughed.

'I'm afraid not,' she said cheerfully. 'I was educated at a School for young ladies, and excelled only in sport – tennis in the summer and hockey in the winter. We have a fine Old Girls' team now, and lose practically every match we play. But we get covered in mud and thoroughly enjoy ourselves.'

'And tennis?' enquired Mr Everett.

'I'll answer for her game of tennis, sir,' said James. 'We had several games last summer and I can vouch for it that she is very quick and has a pretty devastating forehand drive.'

'And serves under arm, I suppose?' asked Mr Lawrence.

'I certainly don't,' said Katie.

She glanced towards T H, suddenly aware that she had taken over the conversation, but he gave her a slow and solemn wink. She smiled at him and sat back in her chair, letting the flow of talk continue around her and only occasionally joining in.

As was his custom, T H departed for work at eight o'clock every day. It was a short walk to his office and, like James, he preferred to plan his day before others arrived.

Meg and Katie stayed at the breakfast table, over a second pot of tea – discussing the conversations at last night's supper table and the unfortunate shade of beige of Mrs Everett's dress, which did nothing for her beige complexion and light brown hair.

'The trouble is that we don't have an unlimited choice of ready made dresses in Falmouth,' Meg said. 'Downing's is very good, but they can only stock so much. I want a new dress for the lifeboat event in August; I've tried on all the new summer dresses they have, but either the fit or the colour is wrong.'

'What you really need,' Katie said, 'is a trip up to Glasgow, or even to Edinburgh. Darling's would be sure to have something to suit you.'

'I know.'

Meg sighed.

'I'd love to come up for a stay, but really I'm needed here, and T H hates it when I'm not at home.'

'But Pa would love to see you, and so would Em, and you could visit the wee wife in her pretty little house, as well as doing your shopping. Why don't you ask T H, even for a few days? It would be better if you could stay a fortnight though.'

'I'd love to come – walking down Sauchiehall Street – what a treat that it would be.'

'Why not ask T H anyway? You could come up with me. Oh, go on Meg – it would be such fun, and the journey's a long one on one's own.'

'I think I will. I'll ask T H tonight.'

'Can't you just say you're going?'

'Not really,' Meg said. 'I can't go without his approval. And there's a lot to arrange in the home so that he's comfortable while I'm away. Besides, he pays the fare!'

'Still, I don't see why you have to ask permission – we're in the twentieth century now, don't forget. I know I'd go, if I wanted to.'

'Maybe you would. But think, Katie. I'm so much older than you – almost a generation older, and perhaps I'm old-fashioned in your eyes, but I promised to obey my husband, and my task in life is to look after T H and our household, and I'm quite content with that.'

'Yes, I suppose so.' Katie said. 'But you will ask him?'

Meg smiled.

'Yes, of course I will. I just have to choose my moment.'

5

Katie and Meg set off for Glasgow the following week, taking the morning train from Falmouth, and the night train from London. Unfortunately, the summer heat made travelling uncomfortable.

Murcia
Pollokshields
Wednesday

Dear James –

We arrived all right but simply stewed; the heat was terrible during the day. I enjoyed the night best as I slept like a top and it wasn't too hot then, but Meg was reduced to her flask once or twice, but she's as large as life now and off to town with Emma. It's even hotter here than the sunny south, so I just hope it keeps on as it is doing and not begin to pour next week. So sorry, I forgot to bring up the photos for you. I left them drying on the pad, so I suppose Tom will notice them.

Father asked if I had forgotten the way home. It was such a treat to see Em again. She looked so cool and airy. We were perfect pigs when we arrived in.

*I hope you are managing to exist and **don't let those seats tempt you!** Tom hasn't forgiven me for bringing his better half away. He did look so forsaken the whole evening before we left.*

Be sure and let me know when you're coming and don't squander all your fortune on new suits and brown boots.

I tried to find some other notepaper as this is too well known, but Em says it's all used, so there's no help for the wicked. Now I am very busy. My life is not a general holiday as yours is .

Yours sincerely,
Katie.

He was pleased that they had taken the decision on Meg travelling with her. Although Katie said she much preferred to leave Falmouth on the early morning train, crossing London in the early evening, to take the Glasgow sleeper, James felt concerned when she travelled alone on the night train. He could imagine that stuffy little compartment, window tightly closed against the smuts, the rattle and clatter of the journey. No wonder Meg couldn't sleep. Katie was more used to it and regarded herself as a seasoned traveller. Katie's letter, of course, was just as he expected. 'Don't let those seats tempt you' – he remembered and smiled.

And there was a reference to Emma – just a year or two older than Katie, unmarried and living at home. He knew that they depended on each others' company, especially now that Nona, the youngest, had married her Bill.

It was good to get a letter so soon too. On their last evening Katie had suggested that their letters to each other should be written twice a week – hers on Tuesdays and Fridays, and his on Wednesday and Saturdays or Sundays. In this way they hoped to grow closer together, in entering, far more, each others' lives and interests.

During the latter part of her holiday, Katie had borrowed Meg's panama for their walks, for the sun had continued to blaze down upon them, and the panama proved the coolest hat to wear.

James had written to Edward who was working in Dunstable, the home of the panama industry. He asked him to send a ladies' panama in this year's fashion, to Katie and of course, sending the bill on to him.

In the meantime, he sent her the photographs he had taken of her in Falmouth, and included the one that she took of him with his own camera.

James and Katie
Falmouth 1905

Murcia, Friday

Dear James,

I got your photos this morning – they're awfully good and thanks very much. Am glad you like mine, and you are extremely taking.

Your manner of overcoming that difficulty was very characteristic. I am quite concerned about your wicked little temper. You ought to learn to govern it e'er it governs you. You might have told me what the man said instead of treasuring it up in the cobwebbie corners of your nasty little soul. You were quite right just to stop him, he never said another thing to me since he told me I was too free. I just ignored him and he didn't seem to relish it.

You say you've been out to two dinners. Don't get fat, James whatever you do. You're not big enough! I suppose you've been busy looking out the window all day? – Katie.

He had hoped she had forgotten about the incident of the man. One evening as they were walking along Grove Place Katie said,

'Oh no, here comes that horrid little man again, with his insulting remarks.'

'What remarks?'

'Och, never mind. He makes comments about my dress, not very polite ones, and then he sniggers.'

They were close to the man now. He was short and shambled along, wearing a threadbare black overcoat, and a shirt open at the neck. No tie.

Sure enough, despite James' presence, he spoke to Katie under his breath. James caught what he said, and swiftly turned to confront him. Katie waited, though she couldn't hear what James was saying. Then the man hurried off, and James rejoined her.

'What did he say?' she asked.

'I shall not tell you.'

'Well, what did you say to him?'

James' face was grim.

'I shall not tell you that either. But I think he won't bother you again.'

They had walked along in silence, until she distracted his attention by asking about the lifeboat, the Bob Newbon, which was moving swiftly across the harbour, and they stood and watched until it disappeared from view.

He was amused by her reference to 'looking out the window all day' – a pastime he could only rarely pursue. He was not so pleased to read 'I'm quite concerned about your wicked little temper.' That was a bit fierce, wasn't it? Yes, he did get annoyed, but only about things that mattered; whereas Katie usually had quite a flippant view of life, unconcerned and light-hearted. It was all a matter of upbringing he supposed, he from a Methodist household, with comparatively elderly parents, and she from a large and obviously wealthy family, yet without a mother.

Walking home to lunch one day he thought of Katie's sometimes sharply worded letters. When she spoke, it was all very amusing. Somehow her words appeared to be critical and severe when writing, not fun at all.

He forgot her though when he found a letter addressed to him lying on the hall table. He had hardly time to pick it up, when Mrs Hocking appeared from the dining room.

'Ah James – a letter came for you in the second post. Oh I see you've noticed it.'

'Yes, I have.'

He glanced at her – her eyes were bright with curiosity, fixed on the envelope in his hand. She came a step closer.

'It says London NW1 on the post mark.'

'Yes, it does.'

He spread out the letter, keeping the envelope between two fingers. He knew the writing – his old friend Easton – whose parents still lived in Falmouth. He was now employed as an assistant at a large pharmacy in Highgate.

Mrs Hocking persisted.

'It looks very like Easton's writing.'

'Yes, it does.'

'Well, what does it say?'

'I haven't read it yet.'

He wondered wrily how much longer he could keep her in suspense. Slowly, he read the first paragraph, both irritated and amused by her probing tactics.

'Not bad news, I do hope?'

'No. It seems to be good news.'

Colour was rising from her neck and suffusing her cheeks in exasperation. Because he was hungry and had to be back in the shop by two, he gave in.

'I'll just wash my hands, then I'll read it to you as we eat.'

He thrust the letter in his pocket and hurried off.

Taking his place at the table, he smiled at his father who was already seated in the carver chair.

'Well now,' he said, 'I'll read you the letter. It's a very nice one and he mentions both of you.'

He unfolded the writing paper and read aloud:

F E Hithervale
134 Highgate
Dispensing and Photographic
London N.W.
Chemist

Aug 8 1905
My Dear James

It is not often I allow myself the honour of a chat with you.

The truth is I'm going to get married and want you to come and see fair play, that is, to be my "Best Man". The event comes off on Wed. Sept. 13th, exactly five weeks tomorrow.

I hope to come home on the 10th, and then we might go up together on the Monday or Tuesday.

You see I quite take it for granted that you will do me that last Bachelor Kindness.

It is to be a morning wedding and although without a doubt there will be a large number at the Service (Union St. Wesleyan Church) the invitations will be restricted to the two families and relatives. However you would be on my relatives bit, whatever capacity you came in. The Service will be followed by Breakfast and the usual Toasts I suppose, and such an accomplished ladies' man will find no difficulty in responding for the Bridesmaids. They will be Miss Minnie Collard and Belle and Lennie.

Say you will come old chap and whether you can induce your mother to accompany you.

With very kind remembrances to both your Father and Mother.

Yours very Sincerely,
Easton.

'How very pleasing', Mrs Hocking said when he had finished. 'I hope he's found an agreeable young lady – and they're to be married at the Wesleyan Church, in Highgate, I presume. It all sound very acceptable.

'And he wants you to come up with me Mother. Do you think you could?'

Mrs Hocking paused.

'I'm afraid not, James. It's a long journey and I don't really want to leave your father.'

'I wouldn't mind,' said Mr Hocking hastily, hoping for a few days of smoking his pipe in the house, instead of being banished to the garden. 'You go if you like, my dear. I can manage very well for a day or two.'

'No, I don't like to leave you,' she said.

This pronouncement successfully quelled any insubordinate ideas that Mr Hocking might be having.

'So please send Easton our best wishes,' she said. 'Well, well, we'll have to find a nice present for him, perhaps a pair of fish servers. I saw some in Fox's the other day. Or, I know, a linen and lace tablecloth I saw in Mrs Best's in Killigrew Street on the way home from my meeting. Tablecloths are always useful. And what about you, James?'

'I haven't had time to think yet. But I'll definitely accept his invitation. Perhaps a mantel clock from Joseph Wearnes – I'll see.'

Then arrived the unhappy news that the new panama had been delivered, but did not fit. Apparently it was too small and "sits like a pimple on top of my head. Em did laugh". James immediately wrote to Edward asking what could be done about it. He received a telegram from Edward next day.

Falmouth Au 12 05
Handed in at Dunstable at 5.34 p.m.   Received
here at 5.50 p.m.
To: Hocking c/o Wilmer Strand Falmouth
No need exchange take leather out. Edward.

This speedy action caused James to write the same
evening to Katie, with Edward's instruction. No letters
appeared for several days until on the seventeenth a
letter arrived at the shop, from Edward.

Dunstable
16.8.05

Dear James,
    Your letter to hand this morning. I am sorry the
hat is not quite right, however I think when the
leather band is taken out it should be quite big
enough in the head. It was a tight 6¾ and when it
is let out I should think it would be a size larger.
    As to the shape: it is the very latest. Ladies'
hats are rather different from Gents. The brim
should not be so wide, and so that makes the crown
look a little higher. When I said about blocking to
other shapes, I meant if the style should alter, say
next year, but that is the only shape being made
now. Of course it can be blocked and made larger
in the crown if necessary, but that would make the
brim still smaller. You had better impress upon
her that it is the most fashionable Panama about.
If she cares to line it with silk she can; she knows
how to do that I dare say.
    I am glad she likes the trimming. I am afraid it
would be difficult to change it now, as it is rather a

61

favour to get one at all, & I am sure they would not care to be bothered in any way. Shall hope to hear a better account when she writes next time.

If you haven't already found out about the boats, don't trouble now, as I have decided to come by train. When I wrote I thought perhaps I should start for my holiday in the middle of the week, but now it has been fixed for Sat. 26th, so it would be wasting too much time. Am writing at office so please excuse paper.

Edward.

James wrote at once to Katie giving all the information that Edward had sent, and on the Wednesday, an envelope with the familiar writing arrived at the shop.

Murcia
Tuesday

Dear James,

I was so vexed I had bothered you about the hat as I was told of a place here, quite handy where it can be done easily. You see I thought if it had to be exchanged it would need to be done at once – that's why I wrote you. I can't imagine why I was so stupid in not thinking of this place before. I am generally smart enough – don't smile: I am.

I hope you like my photo, I think it's splendid – my modesty prevents me from saying more. Winkie brought me down from the clouds by saying, "Katie you should try and look like that oftener." However, I forgave her and we shared a slice of melon to show all was forgiven before she took her departure.

Emma is coming home today – and we are both going to spend tomorrow with great friends at Barassey, a very golfie place. So if the weather keeps up as it is today it should be lovely, as the course there is considered ideal and I've never been on it so am glad I'll have a day to see what it's like.

I think it is very nice of your friend to wish you to be his best man – the first bridesmaid will be hoping you're a respectable sort. I've been one twice so I know the sort of feeling quite well. I hope her nerves will stand the shock, poor thing; my sympathy is hers.

Em and I are going to a wedding on Saturday. I think it's really mean of one's friends to get married at the end of the season when one's roses have lost their first bloom. Am trying to get my hat, which nearly broke up the party last time I wore it, to look more hopefully at life. It is a trifle dejected at present. This girl is marrying an Englishman which for a Scottish person shows very bad taste indeed.

It was truly amazing that you did not get the prize at the tournament with such a partner to spur you to noble deeds. I suppose Miss Pawlyn will come in for any that are going. It brought tears to my brown eyes when I looked back and saw myself sitting neglected at that little table like the last rose of summer. Why can't folk mind their own little businesses in this Vanity Fair? It really seemed to disturb them a lot.

You must thank Edward for the trouble he has taken for me – will you please when you write to him next?

It's a good thing your smoking is cut short. That's why you're such an under grown wee monkey – over indulgence and nothing else – Katie.

6

James had been qualified for four years now and he was considering the next step in his career. If he were to marry Katie, he would need a larger income than he was earning now as a junior pharmacist. He would have to assure her father that he would be able to keep Pa's daughter in "the manner to which she was accustomed". With Katie in mind, this was quite a tall order.

He had written to several friends from his training days, asking them if they knew of any likely partnerships, or small independent businesses which might be on the market.

Then, among the flurry of correspondence about the panama he received a letter from Stanley Hickman, an old friend, who was now a junior pharmacist in his father's partnership.

Hickman and Lamb
Market Place
Newbury

Aug 20 1905

Dear Jimmy,

It seems a long time since we have heard anything of one another, and so I thought I would take up the pen and do my duty.

I hope the world is using you well – for me it is full of worries. The Pater thinks soon of getting out of the Biz and on me devolves the duty of either carrying on or not, & I know not what to do.

You see Harry Lamb is still in the biz and I do not at all relish the idea of partnership with him, &

if I don't go in, it would mean, I suppose, the Biz being sold. It is Mr Lamb's (Senior) intention to be in it for about another 1½ years, I believe.

It seems a pity that a good concern like ours should be sold and yet I feel that I can't go into partnership with Harry Lamb.

Ours is a frightfully worrying business & to tell the truth I long for a business of my own, and if only I had the capital, I should not be long in making up my mind.

And how have you been getting on, old man – I hope well & that your people are well. We have been for our holiday – had good weather and an enjoyable time.

Any chance of your coming this way? If so, don't fail to let me know as we should be very pleased to see you.

The wife is very well, I'm glad to say and also little Joan who is 3 years old now. We are still at Penlee – the garden has looked very well this summer and we have a splendid show of grapes.

If you should happen to hear of a really good business for sale your way, let me know – most unlikely things happen sometimes and perhaps we could work something together – who knows?

By-the-bye, that poor chap Devereaux is to be hanged on Tuesday - & he was at H.H. & Co. before us – you will perhaps remember hearing Pellow and Cox speak of him.

Well, old chap, must close with kind regards to you and yours – in which the wife joins.

Yrs. v. truly
Stanley Hickman

Stanley – it was good to hear from him – they'd had some great times together in London, but then of course they'd gone their separate ways, James to Wilmers, and Stanley to join his father's business in Newbury. Now it seemed that the partnership was at crisis point. James had met young Harry Lamb several times and could understand Stanley's reservations about him, and the difficulties of a partnership with him after their fathers had retired. It seemed Harry took a too light hearted view of his pharmaceutical responsibilities, came in to work late and demanded many times off in the cricket season. Stanley did not approve of his fondness for alcohol either. Customers were not impressed by a whiff of whisky breathed at them across the counter.

James would have liked to go up to Newbury and discuss problems and prospects with Stanley, and to stay with him and his wife at their neat little house on the downs. When he'd been before, the house was very new, and Stanley had been grappling with the garden; he had built a rockery and had ordered a small greenhouse. So that side of his life seemed to be very happy and settled. Yet now he was facing the fact that if he didn't go into partnership, the whole business might have to be sold. What a disappointment that would be to Stanley's father, a pleasant old chap, James had thought.

Perhaps later in the year he might manage a weekend to visit them and then they could have a real exchange of ideas. One thing was certain, James had not heard of any businesses for sale, good or bad, in Cornwall. And to be honest, he really needed to stay in Falmouth. His parents were elderly – his father hadn't married until he was in his fifties. His mother was twenty years younger. Obviously they would need more help as time went on, and as Edward was now in Dunstable, it was he, James, who must look after them.

After they had closed on Saturday evening, he hurried to meet Edward's train, and walked home with him, carrying his case. Mother had delayed supper until his arrival, the table laid with the best cloth and her treasured Worcester china.

During his week's holiday, Edward woke late, spent much of the morning chatting with his parents; had walked round the town and along the cliffs in the afternoon, and had several closely fought games of tennis with James.

He found it hard to blend in with his parents' way of life though. He had become used to having a great deal of independence, coming and going as he wished, reading what papers he liked, having friends in to his digs without a lot of questions. He wondered how James put up with it. In some ways, he appeared to have completely given in to his parents' demands. When he asserted himself it led to arguments, annoyance and his mother saying words of the 'you'll only upset your father' variety. Edward stayed on the sidelines and listened, appalled by his brother's lack of freedom.

On the Thursday evening, James had booked a court again for a game of tennis, when his mother announced:

'We'll have a jolly evening, all together, tonight. Now James, open the piano and play that piece by Liszt that you've been practising. Edward will like to hear it.'

She settled herself in her usual chair by the fireplace, with father opposite. There was no fire of course, just a large fan in the grate made out of pink wallpaper. She smoothed out her skirt.

'Fetch me my wrap James – it'll be cool sitting here. It's on the ottoman in the bedroom', she said.

Edward watched him go, meek as a sheep. 'But she'll try him too far one day,' he thought, 'and I bet it'll be about this girl Katie.'

James returned with the grey woollen shawl, which he placed round her shoulders.

He then sat at the piano and played the Liszt, very competently, Edward had to admit. Then mother wanted Edward to play. He was out of practice, there being no piano in his digs at Dunstable, but he stumbled through *The White Rose*. Mother joined in taking the contralto part, booming mellifluously, drowning Father's tenor and competing with James' baritone. On they went, through *Rock of Ages* and *Onward Christian Soldiers* to *Abide With Me* – mother's favourite.

Then it was cocoa and biscuits time – a quarter to ten. She glanced at the clock and bustled off to put the kettle on.

Precisely at ten o'clock, James helped his father to his feet, they said their goodnights and went up to bed.

'I could do with a smoke,' Edward said, and he and James went out into the cool scented garden.

'How's the Scots lassie?' Edward asked.

'Very well. I'm sorry you missed her again. I'd like you to meet her.'

'Yes, and I'm sorry about the hat business, but there wasn't much I could do.'

'Don't worry about it. She's had it modified locally and is now very pleased with it. She's specially taken with the trimming. Thanks for sending me the sample. I know she's very fond of that particular shade of violet. Her sister Emma is her severest critic, and she approves.'

'I hope she doesn't want to order one as well?'

'Not as far as I know, but the Carswell girls are a determined clan.'

They lit their cigarettes, hoping to keep the gnats at bay. It was nearly dark. White cosmos floated like ghosts in the border.

'Are you serious about her?' Edward asked.

'Katie? Yes, I think so. She has a sort of light hearted attitude to everything which is really cheering.'

'I gather Dad and Mother don't approve?'

'No they don't. They've taken a real dislike to her, on hearsay alone.'

'They're not trusting your judgment then?'

'Far from it. Mother seems to rely on her friend Mrs Kitto's opinion more than mine – all based on Katie's choice of dress. I've asked several times if I could bring her in to tea when she's down here, but Mother always has some reason as to why it would be impossible on the dates I suggest.'

'So Mother hasn't met her yet?'

'Oh yes,' said James, drawing on his cigarette so that the tip glowed brightly in the dusk. 'Meg Sandry, Katie's sister you know, they live at Pendennis House – introduced Katie to Mother after chapel one Sunday. Sparks flew. Mother was so rude. I was very embarrassed and Katie, who is very loyal to her family, reacted as she had every reason to do. That little clash hasn't made matters any easier. I still shudder when I think of it.'

'Is there anything I can do? Speak to Mother or something?'

James paused, blew a spiral of smoke into the dusk and thought of bright little Katie laughing up at him when they'd been splashed by the waves crashing against the rocks near Pendennis Point.

'Thanks for the offer, but I don't think you can help at the moment. I'm hoping that time might improve matters when they see I'm determined and she isn't the loose kind of girl they think she is.'

'Well, let me know if anything turns up that I can do.'

Their neighbours' white cat distracted them momentarily as it bounded down from the wall and strolled across the lawn as if they weren't there, disappearing into the dark under the Hockings' prize camellia.

'Actually, I've just thought of something. Katie is very keen for me to go up to Scotland. The whole family has a holiday in an hotel at Loch Katrine; her father gathers them all together and off they go. But it would be difficult for me to get leave in August, what with the shop being so busy and I do all the developing of the films. But I'd really like to go up there. The fat would be in the fire if the parents knew, so if I could say I was going to stay with you, perhaps you'd forward letters and so on?'

'I'd be glad to. I'd really like to meet your Katie someday.'

They doused their cigarette ends in the bird bath, threw them in the bin and went indoors.

7

Murcia
Tuesday. Aug 22

Dear James,

I got your letter last night and noticed you had written on Saturday night – you must have been worn out, If you can't write on Sundays, just wait until the beginning of the week, as it is far too much for you to write after such a long day as Saturday is for you always.

We had a very jolly time at the wedding, which passed off very well and the bride looked lovely and so did the Misses Carswell.

We went on to the tennis where there was a tournament so I completed the day by presenting the prizes. Nona was in the final but was put out at the end. There is an American tournament on every night this week; you play with the same partner every night and those who have the most points at the end of the week get the prize – so everyone is on and it keeps up the interest.

I have a very good player so we have a good chance, but will need to give a big handicap so may not be near the top after all. However it is most exciting and the weather is splendid and that is the main thing.

Winkie is so comic. She was cycling t'other day with Em and confided to her that she wished to die, so it started raining and commenced to thunder at which she got most scared – so Em said, Well you wished to end your life, here's lightning - perhaps sent to bring you your wish. Winkie roared with

72

laughter and has not since been so eager to go upstairs.

Was glad to read that you had a cup of tea with Mrs T.H. It is certainly better to keep on the weather side of that worthy couple in case of favours wanted in the future. It must be nice for you having Edward home. Be sure and thank him for all the trouble he took, and tell him I am creating quite a stir in the neighbourhood in it.

What a glorious day we had to go to Barrassey – it was just dreamy. They are such nice girls and very old friends of ours, so we had a rare round of golf and a fine gossip afterwards. Their mother is such a pet, simply thinks everything they say or do is perfect, so of course whey worship her in return.

Unfortunately I have hurt my shoulder again a little, but if it doesn't get worse I'll manage all right.

I think it would be nice for you to go into partnership with a friend and then you'd have a better idea and not be taken in as you might be with a stranger. It would be nice for you to get something fixed up and very much easier for me as I never know when Pa will get hold of some of your epistles from the postman, but he hasn't up to date so I can't complain.

We are expecting two Americans on Saturday till Tuesday, a mother and daughter so hope they will make themselves agreeable. We will need to trot them round the country a bit.

Now James I must be off. Hope I can play but my neck is so stiff – it may cure it –

Sincerely yours.
Katie.

73

'Have you actually finished that letter?' Em asked. 'I'm sitting here knitting – I've done half the sleeve and you've just scribbled on and on. It's to James I suppose?'

'Yes.'

'I thought so by the way you keep smiling to yourself. I hope you've thanked him for the panama?'

'Of course I have – ages ago – and again today. Actually I've been telling him about these Americans. Where are you going to put them?'

'I thought in the yellow and green rooms. They're not very big, but I thought they'd enjoy the view of the garden more than the road, if I'd put them in the blue room at the front. I wonder where Pa wants us to take them?'

'He left that to us, surely? Well, let's think. Round the park for a start. I walked through it from Nona's yesterday and it was looking grand – the roses near the gates are superb. Then there's the Art Galleries for a touch of Glasgow culture and a shopping spree in town. I've not heard of an American yet who doesn't love shopping.

'Perhaps we could take the train out to Barrassey,' Emma suggested.

'Good idea, as long as it's a fine day. It'd be a wee bit miserable in a downpour.'

Katie turned back to her letter, skimming through it to make sure James wouldn't find too many mistakes in her spelling – he never missed one – and put it into the envelope.

'I'll just go and post my letter. Have you anything to go?'

'You could take my letter to the folks at Barrassey. I included you in my heartfelt thanks. I hope that's all right?'

'Fine, though I must write to them myself.'

Katie hurried out to catch the post at the corner of the road. When she returned she found Bessie was already bringing in the tea – teacakes, well-buttered, and yesterday's Dundee cake.

The cake reminded Emma to make sure there was a new one made for the visitors. They sat together, amicably chatting over the tennis prospects for the end of the season.

'James says they often play right through until October,' Katie said.

'Really? I suppose it's so much warmer. Too cold up here though. Shall I cut you a slice?'

'Yes, please. In his last letter he's told me that he's started to look for a partnership, or possibly his own small business. He's written to one or two friends who were training with him to see if there are any prospects with one of them.'

'I'm glad,' Emma said. 'I mean, if he's really thinking of a house and marriage he'll have to be earning a decent salary.'

'Yes,' said Katie, 'but is he?'

'I don't know any more than you do. After all I've never met him. What do you think?'

Katie was silent for some time.

'I think he is. We've talked about it a lot this holiday. Oh Em, I'd love to have my own house in Falmouth. There's so many pretty terraces and squares. And Meg's such a dear. I could always run down to see her for a sound of home. And most of all, I would be with James for ever – no more endless journeys to and fro.'

'Well don't run on too far ahead. This is the first step, the very beginning. And his folks don't sound very helpful.'

Katie grimaced.

'They're not. I told you about the fracas at the church door? They seem to have James well drilled into submission, especially his mama. But at least he showed a bit of independence when Meg invited him to supper.'

Emma cut herself a second piece of cake.

'It's funny, isn't it?' she said, gathering up the crumbs and popping them into her mouth. 'You always read about the English calling us the "dour Scots", but I've never heard of anybody quite as dour as you say they are.'

'But they're proper Cornish,' said Katie, 'and they're a breed apart.'

'Meg seems to like them, anyway.'

'She does indeed. But then, she married a Cornishman. He came from Porthleven originally and sometimes they go over there to see some of his cousins. Meg says it's a lovely spot, so nice she'd like to retire there,' Katie said, ' if you can imagine Meg retiring.'

'Didn't she enjoy herself here though, when she came back home with you?'

'Indeed she did.'

Meg had had a marvellous time in Glasgow. She had forgotten how noisy and bustling this great city was – its hurrying crowds crossing the bridges, dodging the trams, and the horses and carts weaving in and out of the other traffic. Everything was different from Falmouth, even the robust Glasgow voices compared with the gentle Cornish burr.

It was wonderful to catch up with her sisters too. One day she went out to Largs to see Jane and her family. At first she was shocked to find Jane looking so much older, until she looked in the mirror and had to admit she looked a little older too. At Murcia she immediately became Pa's favourite daughter again. No one minded that, for they were all his favourites, depending on who most engaged his attention. Meg enjoyed everything, starting with the breakfast baps. She spent some time in the kitchen with Bessie, learning how to make them. The recipe was duly tucked into her luggage to take home.

She made several forays into town. It seemed like old times, walking through George Square with a sister either side of her. Winkie went with her to the Art Galleries to see an exhibition of Venetian lace.

Her main objective, though, was to find a suitable summer dress for the lifeboat event. Emma went with her, but Katie, who had wanted to go too, had a tennis match in the afternoon and her shirt to mend before she went.

'That's what comes of serving over arm,' Emma said, and Katie threw the cotton reel at her.

They tried some of the larger stores for the perfect dress without any success. Everything seemed to be in heavy satins this season, and Meg wanted something lighter, perhaps a voile or light cotton. Then she thought of a small salon in Buchanan Street.

'You won't remember Madame Patrice,' she told Emma, 'but I was always lucky there. I hope she's still in business.'

She was. They stood before the small frontage and gazed at the window display – a solitary model clad elegantly in pale lemon silk, the colour echoed in a single beautiful arrangement of yellow roses.

'Well, shall we go in?'

Emma followed her in to the shop. Meg was served by Madame Patrice in person, who listened attentively to her description of the dress she had in mind.

'Ah' said Madame 'I really think I can help you. One moment please. Perhaps you would take a seat, while I make some choices for you.'

She left the salon. Meg and Emma perched side by side on a chaise longue and waited, inclined to giggle in the silence.

'I hope that all this won't be too expensive,' Meg murmured. 'It all seems grander than it used to be.'

'Well if it is,' Emma said, 'you'll just have to say you've changed your mind.'

But Madame returned with a thin young woman dressed in a simple light silk, white with a sky blue check. She advanced towards them, giving Meg an opportunity to feel the material, turned so that Meg could have a back and side view.

Meg was silent, entranced.

'I have other designs if you don't favour zis one,' suggested Madame.

'This is exactly what I had in mind,' Meg replied. 'I was even thinking that blue would be a pleasant choice.'

'It comes with zis,' said Madame, whisking a matching cape from the chair where she had dropped it.

She arranged it on the model's shoulders, and they admired the frill of blue silk ribbon which edged the cape.

'And zis,' said Madame, opening a drawer.

She took out a blue lacy hat trimmed with white spotted net frills, wide and graceful.

'Try it,' offered Madame.

Even Emma gasped when she saw Meg putting it on.

'You look beautiful', she said. 'It's exactly the colour of your eyes.'

Meg made the decision. Madame promised that the dress would be sent to Falmouth, once it was made to Meg's measurements, within the next three weeks. She then led Meg away to be measured. As every detail was vital to the fit of the dress, this took some time.

Finally the bill was paid, the hat was tissue wrapped into a hat box, and they left the shop.

'I think I need a cup of tea', said Meg.

'And so do I', said Emma. 'What a lovely outfit, Meg.'

They sank into the high backed chairs in the Buchanan Street Ladies; Tea Rooms. Meg admired anew the stained glass screens and stencilled walls and doors.

'I'm afraid there's nothing as elegant as this in Falmouth,' she said.

They drank tea and indulged in creamy meringues, watching the gossiping customers at other tables.

At home, Meg tried on the hat again to show Katie and Nona, who had just returned from the tennis match.

'Wonderful,' Katie said, 'T.H. will love it.'

Pa came in and stopped abruptly in the doorway.

'My dear little Meg,' he said. 'You look exactly like your beautiful mother.'

For a moment they were all taken aback. Then Pa blew his nose and wiped his eyes and the spell was broken.

'Just in time for the first cup of tea, Pa,' Katie said, as Bessie bustled in with a heavy tray, landing it hard on the table so that all the china rattled.

'O my deary me, Miss Meg,' she said, 'where ever did you find that hat? Nearly made me drop the tray, it did. I thought for a moment it was dear Mrs Carswell come back to life again. You're the spit image of her.'

79

8

Summer had slipped into autumn and the last of the tennis was over, the nets and posts cleaned and stored for winter and a committee meeting convened to tidy up the last of the business and to note one or two ideas that would make for even better running of the club in 1906.

Falmouth hostesses began to plan their evening gatherings. Whist drives and dances were anticipated now that the summer visitors had drifted home.

In mid September a neat card was delivered to the shop, to Mr J Hocking, in a flowery hand. The card read:

FALMOUTH DANCING CLUB

The Committee of the above requests the pleasure of Mr J. Hocking's Company to a class to be held at the Polytechnic Hall, on Monday evenings, from 7.45 to 10 p.m., commencing on Monday, the 16th October, 1905.

Subscription for Season, 5/-; Occasional Members, 1/- per night.
R.S.V.P. on or before Saturday 7th October, 1905 to the secs:-

E. Dunning, Fish Strand
H. Rowe, Strand.
H. Dawe, Treasurer.

Dancing classes? Mondays? Well, not much happened on Mondays; most of the evening parties were held on

Wednesdays (half day closing), Friday or Saturday nights. Accordingly he sent off two half-crowns to Mr Dawe, and a reply to Mr Rowe. He always enjoyed all the sets of the Lancers, with the old music and the variety of patterns the dancers' feet trod as they wove the intricate steps. He needed to brush up on the Quadrille too, before the winter season began in earnest.

However there were more serious matters on James' mind. For some time he had been considering owning his own business. He was twenty seven, time now to be independent. If he were to buy a business, this would be an excellent time to do it, while he was young and active and full of ideas. Furthermore, if he were to marry Katie he would need an income that would support the purchase of a house, and a future likely to be satisfactory financially to Katie's father. He knew also that Katie would not be an inexpensive wife. She had not been brought up to consider economies.

There were so many things in the shops he had worked in during his apprenticeship, and now at Mr Wilmer's, that he longed to change. There was lunchtime closing. Most shops closed from one till two o'clock, but he was sure there could be a surge of customers then, as they made their way home to lunch and back to work again. There was a fortune to be made on indigestion cures alone, he thought. Then there was the matter of working hours. Miss Hawke worked through the day till six o'clock, sitting in the back dispensary to eat her pasty during the lunch hour. How much more sensible it would be if she stayed on late duty night, and took an extra half day, perhaps on Tuesdays, which was usually a slack day.

The windows needed attention too. Mr Wilmer cluttered them up with dozens of bottles that gathered dust from the streets and the quay, their labels fading rapidly in the strong sunlight. James had suggested alterations, but they were not taken up by Mr Wilmer. James pictured each of the five windows surmounted by a carboy on each top shelf and then each window devoted to one special aspect – Kodak show cards, for instance, with one or two cameras; mother and baby requirements, cosmetic powders, teeth, Heath and Heather herbal preparations and so on. He would change the photographic dark room too, from the tiny room, little more than a cupboard, to the back store room which was seldom used but had more than adequate space.

Stanley Hickman's letter had triggered this line of thought, but he had no intention of finding himself with an incompatible partner. Nothing could be worse than to have one's working hours shared with someone whose views were not in line with his own.

He cast about wondering where he could find out about likely premises for sale. Disquieting rumours had reached him via other traders in the town that Timothy White and Taylor's , and Boots also had designs on setting up in Falmouth. But how could he find out if these rumours were true?

He had noticed an advertisement in the pharmaceutical press for a one-man business which was for sale in Paignton, Devon. He sent for further details, chiefly in order to discover the going price, profit and turnover of a business of this size.

Eventually, needing his bank passbook updating, he decided to write to his bank manager friend in Newquay to see if his savings could be put to better use if invested in different companies. The reply from Bertie came quickly.

Devon & Cornwall Banking Company Limited,
Newquay
October 1st 1905.

Dear James,

Your passbook to hand which I return herewith made up to date.

With regard to a Deposit or investment it remains with you as to what you would like, but if you want something safe & to return about 4% why not wait a little longer till you can raise £95 or so & have one of our shares at the price they will yield £4. 4/-. I expect you would have to have it in joint names with Edward the same as others but presume you would not mind that. Or if you fancy something different I think Harrods Stores at about £4 paying 5% are alright, or Lyons & Co. at £6¼ paying £4.15%. I have just bought a few of these myself as I rather fancy they will rise before long – I have £6 1/16 and they have moved up a bit since to about 6¼.

Then again Lever Bros 5% cumulative preference shares (Sunlight Soap) at 12½ yield £4% but they are quite high enough just now and I shouldn't wonder if they get a bit easier sooner or later.

If you fancy something a little more speculative and returning high dividends there is "Illustrated London News and Sketch" at 10/- a share dividends last year were 8%.

Remember these shares are usually bought and sold in fives – that is 5-10-15 or 25-30 etc.

Evelyn and Doris have gone to Truro today. They have both had colds, but are better now.

I hope you are all keeping well
Yours sincerely to your people,
Bertie.

P.S. I shan't touch any more S.S. shares as for the
last few years they can't be depended on.

A few days later James was preparing to leave the shop –
an early night – it was now ten past six, when Mr
Wilmer called him back.

'James,' he said. 'as you know I have been thinking
of retiring for some time and selling the business. I
should like to travel a bit more, and to have more leisure
to do the things I'd really like to concentrate on – bridge,
for instance, the garden and my boat. I think from the
little you've said to me on the subject, that you might
like to buy the business. Am I right?'

James was astonished.

'Why, yes sir, I certainly am interested.'

'Good. Well we can go into details later. It's been a
good concern, and I pride myself on building it up to
what we have today. The lease is up for renewal in the
next year or so and that could be a good time to have a
change of ownership.'

'Could you give me an idea as to how much you are
thinking of selling for?'

Mr Wilmer took out his tin of tobacco, selected one
of his collection of pipes that had their own stand on his
desk, and began to fill it in a leisurely way. James was
in an agony of suspense. He could well imagine that the
price would be way beyond his ability to pay.

'Well now,' said Mr Wilmer, drawing on his pipe
with every appearance of satisfaction. 'I need to get a

thorough valuation done, audit of stock, the position with regard to the lease, and so on. But I've compared it with other similar businesses during the last year or so, and I think we're looking at about £2,000, and I'd like to sell up within the year. Oh, and by the way, I have a law suit coming up – it's regarding some property I own up country. I'm fully expecting it to be settled in my favour, and so then I'll be in a good position to retire.'

James' hopes dived. Two thousand pounds – a terrific amount of money. How could he hope to acquire it in the time limit that Mr Wilmer had just indicated?

'May I have a few days to think it over?' he asked. 'It's a marvellous opportunity for me, and I am grateful to you for giving me the chance to buy. But I certainly need to talk it over with my family. Would you allow me a few days to think it over, get advice from my bank manager and so on?'

'Of course, my dear boy. These matters can't be settled in a few minutes. But I'd be pleased if you'd come back to me with something definite - yea or nay – say, within the next month. After that I shall advertise in the Journal.'

James walked home along Market Street in a whirl of conjecture, answering several greetings abstractedly. He'd await a good moment to mention the matter to his father and mother. But first thing to do would be to write to Bertie Orchard immediately, ask his advice, ask him if he'd heard any rumours about Boots or Timothy White's opening in Falmouth. From the business point of view, he knew Bertie couldn't be beaten over the care he took in making suggestions.

After supper he put off his mother's request to go over the music of a new hymn.

'Later mother,' he said. 'I've one or two letters to write first and I'd like to get them off as soon as possible.'

She looked suspiciously at him, but forbore to ask with whom he was corresponding.

Bertie's reply came by return post.

Devon & Cornwall Banking Company Limited,
Newquay
November 30th 1905.

Dear James,

I can quite imagine you have been both excited and worried. I should be pleased to give you any advice within my power, but of course I'm not supposed to know a great deal about Chemists' profits – what they should be in relation to turnover, for instance.

Anyhow there are several ways of looking at this thing and I wish I could chat to you rather than write about it.

It seems to me Wilmer is looking for too high a figure for his business but you do not say what the price includes – does it include a lease of present premises, stock etc., and if so what is the value of stock and fittings included? As far as I know the shop is not fitted up very grand in the way of fittings – certainly not like the shops are here – your window has always struck me as being rather shabby and I should very soon turn that upside down, to keep up with the times – a smart appearance goes a long way nowadays. The net profit seems very small compared with turnover, but perhaps it is being worked expensively, and I have not understood that Mr W exerts himself at all so perhaps it could be worked with one less assistant if the proprietor turned in to work here.

I should consider £1500 to be the utmost value and that is then about 4 years purchase of the net profits – surely quite enough if there is likelihood of opposition.

Rather than pay such a big sum as £2,000, I would pick out a good opening in some other town and work up a business of my own and keep the money in my pocket.

With regard to the Paignton business – Paignton is a nice spot and the people are well-to-do- but I don't know what opposition you would have there and why the chap is giving up. I will make an enquiry for you privately through our Bank and let you know.

I shouldn't look at it unless the lease can be renewed. I think the net profits in the case seem more in proportion to the turnover but I don't think I should be tempted to give the price asked.

Of course the whole thing needs very careful looking into and there are many points to be considered. You would of course have a thorough examination of the books and I think I could put you up to a good many things to be gone into if you seriously entertain any particular business.

Can't write any more at present – will write when I hear from Paignton.

Cheque £10 to hand for your account.

Love to all,
Yours sincerely –
Albert J Orchard.

James felt rather cast down having read this cautious missive. Then he remembered Mr Taylor, the former bank manager whom he had consulted when he was at Newquay. He wrote to him, asking a number of questions, and quickly received a reply.

1/12/05

Mayfield,
Park Place,
Exeter

My dear Mr Hocking,
Re yours to hand which is certainly very remarkable in the information you convey.
First, re Boots – I must correct your misapprehension about their "prospecting" Falmouth among other towns. If you recall aright you will remember I said that I thought Messrs Timothy White would have their eye on Redruth, Penzance and Falmouth. This is of course only a surmise of my own and have heard nothing from anybody of it.
Is it the firm in question do you think, of whom you have heard a whisper, that they have bought the Café Royal, and not Boots? Can you not "fish out" to whom the property has been sold (if sold at all)? Of course firms go in a quiet way to work in such cases – fir instance I heard that the Truro shop for Timothy White's was bought through a solicitor and the vendors didn't know for whom intended.

And now to the next and most important item in your letter, viz – the offer to sell for £2,000 by Mr Wilmer. The reason he assigns of course is a good reason for not wishing to remain in business – that is if the lawsuit means that property will be coming to him through the decision in his favour.

Well now, as to its value, you should know best of all, and can compare it with the Paignton concern. I asked my friend Parsons to look into this for you, but he's not a prompt correspondent and I have not heard from him yet. I hope to see him on Tuesday week and will then of course report accordingly. Meanwhile I will try to find out if anyone has heard whether Timothy White has any idea of Falmouth. Of course I quite see your point – viz: as to the value of a business being lowered by such a near competition. (if it really came off). Have you asked John Blamey if he has heard anything?

This I think completes my comments on your letter. If any further developments I should be glad to be informed.

With kind regards to your father and mother and yourself.

Believe me
Yours very truly
T.J. Taylor

If there was one single thing that was abhorrent to James it was "fishing out" information that was essentially private. This was to him a very underhand way of going on, and until now he had not been aware that seemingly this was how business could be done. But he realised that if he was firmly interesting in buying Wilmer's, this is what he must do.

He considered the men of his acquaintance who might be in the know; Mr Wilmer might have heard something, or perhaps Mr Sandry. Next he thought of a solicitor – he would have to instruct one if he were to go ahead with the purchase. Over the next week he made enquiries, but all the possible sources of information were unaware of either chain of chemists being actively interested in starting up in Falmouth. So that was one hurdle cleared.

Unfortunately, all the tension of the enquiries, compounded with Mrs Hocking's tenet that "every man needs three good meals a day" resulted in a bout of indigestion worse than James had ever experienced before.

He wrote to Katie, telling her of the possibilities of owning his own business; they had discussed this during the summer and she had been keenly interested.

'Take Pa as an example,' she had said. 'He started out as a draper's assistant and saved as much of his pay as he could after giving his mother money for his keep. So it wasn't many years before he was able to set up on his own, and had two men working for him. He bought and sold watch material. He was only twenty five then.'

'The same age as I am give or take a year,' James said ruefully.

'Well yes. Quite an example wasn't he? Then, because he was keen on fly fishing – always away to the rivers whenever he had the opportunity, he got started on making fishing tackle. He was married of course by then and had five children. One little boy died. Anyway, Pa had forty three girls and twenty one men working for him. Meg remembers it well. She says he had boundless energy and worked all hours. Whenever he saw an opportunity, he took it. Oh, he's old now, of course, but he still enjoys going down to the office every day.'

'I'd have hard work living up to that example,' he had said.

In the letter, James also mentioned that he had had terrible indigestion. Katie was not sympathetic.

Murcia
Friday

Dear James,

I hope your indigestion is behaving itself again. Of a truth you should try and cultivate a more romantic and aristocratic ailment. Why do you persist in overeating yourself? I really can't sympathise with a man who allows his lower nature to predominate as you do. Or I daresay you've been dosing yourself with your awful pills – no wonder you suffer, poor thing.

Everybody is home now, Harry among them, so the place has resumed its usual aspect again. But the weather is horrible.

I don't seem to have any news today and am in a very bad mood for letter writing, that's why I've been kind of "making conversation" as I go along, and I ought to be brilliant as I am just expecting to see Bessie appear with the afternoon tea any moment. Now here it comes and you know I always told you that you were nothing compared to a cup of tea, so I must draw this interesting epistle to a timely close, hoping it will find you on the one

meal a day system. I would recommend it to you
very strongly. Katie.

James, still having severe indigestion pain, thought it might have been better if Katie had not written at all if this was an example of being not in the mood for writing letters. Usually he took her flippant remarks at face value, as she would have spoken them in her playful and inconsequential way. But this letter he found neither amusing nor sympathetic. H didn't read it again, merely placing it in the box when he went up to the attic, first taking another dose of stock anti-gastric acid mixture. Temporarily, he felt better, and tackled the account books that Mr Wilmer had lent him in order to judge for himself the state of the business.

9

Katie wrote again on October 17th 1905:

Murcia
Tuesday

Dear James,
Such a pity you didn't get to miss morning service – the powers unseen evidently consider you require all the sermons you can get and I have no doubt the powers unseen are correct.

So you have never heard of a butterfly's wing? I expect your wee cranium is merely stored with things you shouldn't know – when you wish to pose as a small eater – a sort of fairy above such earthly things as food you say – oh! you've just dined off a butterfly's wing. Have I made it quite clear? I must remember in future not to wander on the mountain tops but to keep in the valley where you can follow without difficulty. What a well-informed mite you will be in time – you owe me a debt of gratitude which increases every week!

What a soaking we got on Saturday. It looked fine so I put on a new blouse. No sooner had we arrived when it poured. They wanted to play so we did till we were so wet and I was nearly crying with cold, that we retired into a cottage where a lovely fire made us leap for joy – and had two hours to wait for a train – horrible!

Mrs Wilmer didn't write but it wasn't necessary for such a slight thing at all – because I had promised them one before I left.

I trip the light fantastic toe on Friday evening and am hoping to create a stir – may disappointment not be mine – why aren't you going? You might then be able to teach me the Lancers. I remember you once offered to instruct me. However I expect I shall have to flounder through untaught.

Emma is going to the theatre that night with Bill and Nona, so she won't be left on her lonesome.

We begin our hockey tomorrow at half two and then we've a match on the 26th so we've not long to get into form at all, and my blouse isn't finished so I hasten to put in the last stitches – it will be a faithful friend through mud and rain for many months.

We're going off to a teafight in the church tonight – a sociable where you're supposed to talk to folk you don't like and give tea to those who wickedly abuse you.

Goodnight – Katie O.

Over the next two months James' letters became short and scrappy, mainly because he was beset by all the work and problems associated with the purchase of the business. Many evenings were spent in his little room in the attic tussling with profit and loss, future estimations and the problem of raising the necessary finance.

He was sorry that he hadn't had an opportunity to teach Katie the Lancers. She was a good dancer, light on her feet and quick to learn. He could imagine future dances in Falmouth where he would partner her through all the sets. The music was attractive too, and, like him,

Katie loved music of all kinds, from dance music to oratorio, from street musicians to grand opera.

But all that would have to wait now until she came down again next summer. It seemed an age away.

As Christmas approached the shop grew busier. Elegant bottles of perfume arrived, ordered long ago in the summer, as well as brushes and combs, scented soaps wrapped for the Christmas season and manicure tools in small leather cases.

Saturdays, always busy, became quite frantic as the weeks went by. An extra assistant would have been more than welcome at this time of the year, but, as Mr Wilmer pointed out to James, an assistant without training in the intricacies of the business, would be more of an encumbrance than use.

The windows took on a festive appearance also, and this was a job allotted to James. Some years earlier Mr Wilmer had been at work on the Christmas window. Unfortunately, unable to ease the cramp in his thigh which had been brought on by the awkward position he had been in, kneeling as he reached the front of the window, he stood up suddenly, cracking his head sharply on the high shelf on which the carboys stood. The vibration of the shelf caused a carboy to wobble, and then, to his horror, it had crashed down through the window. Glass was strewn over the pavement and the gutters ran scarlet with the contents of the carboy. Since this disaster Mr Wilmer had retired from window dressing and was pleased to find that James enjoyed it.

Wednesday afternoon, early closing day, was the time James chose to do the window. There were no customers to distract him and the street was relatively quiet. He cleared out the current display of cold and cough cures, steam kettles and inhalers and cleaned the shelves. He had the replacements ready and made a

95

colourful display of elegant coffrets containing soap, bath salts and talcum powder. Bath salts – quite unnecessary in the soft Cornish water – made a pretty gift. Hair brushes and combs were arranged with Yardley's brilliantine, lavender scented, on the floor of the window. When it was completed, James surveyed the result from outside on the pavement. There was a blank spot at eye level, so he hurried indoors, for a cold rain was falling, and filled it with an Atkinson's show card and an array of their flower perfumes – rose, lily of the valley, sweet pea and violet.

Outside again, he was pleased to see how well the Atkinson's addition had completed his scheme. It cheered a grey afternoon.

Letters from Katie continued to irritate him. It seemed that she thought he had another lady friend – or at least she kept alluding to that suspicion in her letters. He had ceased to try to defend himself for she would not be placated. Instead of keeping her letters in the wooden box, he read each one carefully, twice, before consigning it to the dispensary fire. He had no wish for his mother to find the letters in one of his pockets – the outcome would be incendiary indeed and rather hotter than the fire at the shop.

For her Christmas present, he chose a china dressing table tray that he had noticed in one of their trade catalogues. It had a pearly lustre glaze and was decorated with a flight of blue birds.

In her present mood, Katie might well accuse him of taking the easy way of present buying, but that couldn't be helped. He was short of time and beginning to feel short of temper. This was exacerbated by the late delivery of the consignment that included the tray, so that it was almost Christmas before he had packed it and posted it to Scotland.

In Pollokshields, Katie's temper was as volatile as James had gathered from her letters. The weather reflected her moods, heavy sleet and snow showers preventing the hockey team working off some of their surplus energy.

She was alarmed by the brevity of James' letters. Sometimes they didn't arrive on the expected day either.

On this particular Monday, his letter arrived with the morning post, but consisted of one sheet of shop paper, a quarter of which was taken up by the ornate heading.

Emma was sitting at the other side of the table, placidly eating toast and marmalade. Katie had opened the envelope and sat, staring indignantly at the letter.

'Why bother to write at all?' she said.

She screwed up paper and envelope into a ball and tossed it towards the fire. Unfortunately her aim was at fault, and it rolled out onto the hearthrug, which required her to rise, pick it up and stow it in the flames.

'What's the matter?' Emma asked.

'It's James', said Katie. 'There's something wrong I know. He sent me that pretty tray, but only at the last minute. I think the truth of it is that he wasn't going to send me anything, changed his mind and took the first thing he could find off the display shelves.'

'Now, Katie, don't go flying off into one of your tantrums. You've no reason to say things like that.'

'But his letters now are so short and scrappy – they're hardly worth the stamp. He says he's very busy. Maybe he is but he can't be occupied every hour of the day, and so I've told him.'

'Well, if he says he's busy I expect he is', Emma said. 'We're nearly at Christmas and he's told you how busy they get in December. Probably everyone's got coughs and colds and run down to Wilmer's for a bottle

97

of linctus and those awful Thermogene pads that old people wrap around their chests to keep out the cold.

Katie buttered another piece of toast.

'Have you left any marmalade in that pot? Oh good.' She applied the marmalade to the toast and bit into it.

'Yes,' she said, chewing briskly. 'I suppose you're right. But we live so far from each other, it's easy to imagine that he might have found someone else. There are plenty of pretty girls in his neighbourhood, if he likes that 'wouldn't say boo to a goose' kind of lassie.'

Emma considered this, looking at Katie's frowning brow and generally despondent air.

'From all you've told me about him, he doesn't sound the kind of man who'd do that. And even if he did meet someone else, I'm sure he'd find the courage to tell you. No honestly, Katie, I think he is what he says he is – busy. And I'll tell you another thing, while we're on the subject – you need to curb that temper of yours. No good ever comes of it when you fly up in a rage.'

'I'm not in a rage. I'm just upset.'

'I know you are, but sometimes other people don't realise that. And writing letters can be difficult. It's easy to give the wrong impression and people can think you're more vehement than you actually are.'

Katie nodded.

'I know. The other thing of course, is that I can't say what I'd really like to say …'

'What would that be?'

'Well, you know, that I'm very fond of him. But I can't write things like that, it just isn't done. The fat really would be in the fire if Mother Hocking found one of my letters. We have to be so discreet. I live in dread that Pa will meet the postman and ask who wrote the letter from Falmouth. Just imagine, "It doesn't look like

Meg's writing. Whoever is it from?" and he'd open the envelope and have a look.'

'Yes he would. Well, as long as you or I are down first, we should be able to stop that happening.'

They finished their coffee, and Emma went off to oversee the bed linen which went in a wicker basket to the laundry. Katie cleared the table onto Bessie's tray and folded the cloth. Although partly mollified by Emma's remarks, James' brief messages still rankled. If only they could meet and talk, she knew that all misunderstanding would be at an end. Distance was the whole trouble – meeting for a few weeks twice a year put a strain on both of them; it was an intolerable situation. All sorts of difficulties were ranged against them, not least his parents' disapproval. She sighed and gazed out of the window, just in time to see Winkie's tam-o'shanter passing the railings as its owner turned to go up the steps to the front door. Troubles momentarily forgotten, she ran to open the door.

The letters which James received from Katie over Christmas both hurt and annoyed him. The shop was busy, winter coughs and colds and an outbreak of ·'flu kept them all working till long past eight o'clock. He envied Katie, whose father took them all for the New Year to stay at Shandon Hydropathic Hotel, an enormous and elegant mansion with lawns down to the loch. Whilst Pa underwent a regime which included therapeutic baths, for rheumatism, the girls revelled in the house's warmth and played billiards and whist with the other guests. In the mornings they donned their thick coats, fur hats, gloves and boots, and crunched along the loch side, snow underfoot. The sun shone, although it was very cold. They returned to the house with glowing cheeks and a cheerful sense of wellbeing.

Their maid, Bessie, had been given the task of redirecting all their mail to the Hydro. Kate received two brief letters from James and was convinced that he was losing interest in her.

One evening, after Nona and Bill had returned home, Emma and Winkie had made up a bridge foursome with some other residents. Pa had retired to the smoking room with his friends, the air now hazy with tobacco and whisky fumes. Katie found herself without companions. Everywhere she looked, people were happily playing cards or sitting by the drawing room fire chatting over the coffee pot. Some younger guests were laughing over the table tennis table in the play room. She watched for a while, but no one spoke to her or invited her to have a game with them.

Eventually, thoroughly downcast, feeling lonely and unwanted, she went up to her room, found her writing case, and wrote to James. She accused him of finding someone else and of sending her present as an afterthought. She added that he obviously didn't care for her. Her pen drove on ruthlessly into the paper. She addressed, stamped and sealed the envelope. Then she returned to the drawing room, found a comfortable chair and asked for a pot of hot chocolate.

The soothing richness of the chocolate and friendly conversation with a nearby couple soon dispelled her black mood. When eventually she went up to bed, she looked at her letter, regretting her words. She postponed any decision about sending it, deciding that she would make up her mind in the morning.

She slept late, until Emma bounced onto her bed to tell her she'd miss her porridge if she didn't get up straight away.

After breakfast she returned to her room. Her one purpose now was to destroy the letter. How could she have written such cruel things? To her dismay the letter was not on the dressing table where she was sure she had left it. She checked the bedside table, the wash stand, the chaise longue in the bay window. The letter had disappeared. She was still searching for it when Emma came in.

'They're making up a party to drive to the new hotel for lunch,' she said. 'I said we'll go. Off at eleven o'clock.'

'Emma,' Katie said, 'have you by any chance seen a letter? I'm sure I left it on the dressing table?'

'The one addressed to James? I knew you'd want to get it off by the first post, so I took it down with me after I'd woken you up.'

'You mean you posted it?'

'Yes of course. In the letter box in the hall.'

Katie fled down the stairs. The doorman was sorting the incoming mail on the hall table.

'Could you please open the post box? I need to take out a letter I wrote. It was put in by mistake.'

He turned slowly towards her.

'I'm sorry Miss Carswell,' he said, 'the postman emptied the box twenty minutes ago and has gone on his way.'

1906

10
January
1906

James was appalled when he read the mis-posted letter –
appalled, and as he considered it further during the day,
he was very angry. He couldn't understand Katie's
attitude at all. Why, she seemed to have turned him into
some kind of villain. His first inclination was to cease
any communication whatever with her immediately. By
evening however, he had decided to write and refute all
these allegations. When the shop closed he stayed on
and went up to his attic room, turning over in his mind
what he was going to write. He lit the lamp and pulled
the writing paper towards him. He paused. Perhaps it
would be more sensible to write the letter in rough first –
then he would only have to copy it out. He picked up a
pencil and began:

Dear Katie,
Your letter of 3rd just to hand from which it
appears to me that you are not quite certain
whether my statements were correct or not as you
say "give a dog a bad name etc." – I should like to
know why the dog has such a bad name. I am
enclosing a letter from our wholesale house which
will prove beyond all doubt that I had ordered the
tray before you wrote.
In your Murcia letter you refer to a passage in
one of my letters in which I said that I was very
busy on the Saturday before Xmas, that is as just a
reply to one of your remarks saying that you

expected that I was full of nasty bachelor's thoughts on that day. Well you may imagine that on that day is the busiest we have in the whole year – one has to concentrate his thoughts pretty much on his work but I will not say that even then are times when thoughts of friends are in the mind but no time for putting on paper.

I think your letter to me from the Hydro was very unnecessary and very unkind. I cannot understand whatever prompted you to write such. I think you will agree with me that this is the 3rd letter that I have had of this kind which are naturally very upsetting and I think very unfair and I fail to see wherein they have been ...

Whatever led you to suspect that I have found letter writing a bother I cannot understand.

You also said that I could not help not caring and that you could not imagine my interests would remain the same always, you certainly have not a great deal of confidence in me?...

When Katie realised that the letter was irretrievable, she sat down to write again apologising over and over for her appalling behaviour. She wrote that she couldn't explain to him why she had written as she had, and that she had tried to retrieve the letter. She begged him to forgive her.

As an afterthought, she included a post card of Shandon Hydro, and in much more like her usual writing style, she wrote on the back:

The hydro is filled with English folks and we were followed round the links by such a nice wee

Englishman which answered to the name of Jimes
– it reminded me of a certain little village. K.O.C.

The family returned home next day. It had been a cold journey, a thaw having set in and heavy Glasgow rain was falling. A letter awaited Katie from James. She took it upstairs to her room immediately, tore open the envelope and scanned the contents. It began by accepting her apology, rather stiffly but gradually the tone eased and became more informal. She sighed with relief and read it again more slowly, unnoticed tears sliding down her cheeks. Finally, she folded the paper and pushed it back into its envelope and left it in the top drawer of her dressing table. Then she ran downstairs to the warmth of the drawing room where a bright fire blazed and Emma was pouring the tea.

The next morning she had returned to her usual flippant style:

Murcia
5th Jan 1906

Dear James,

I am sorry I have misjudged you in this matter. I don't know how but I didn't really believe what you said – however, I'd rather believe you as not of course, so rest in peace.

I made up my mind to give you the chance of retiring gracefully from the scene of action.

We're just home last night and have had such a good time and the people were all nice so it passed very quickly. On New Year's Day Mary, Em and I took a motor to Crieff Hydro for afternoon tea –

most of our friends were there and had invited us. It was a twenty mile run from ours and it was fine but so cold – we made a fairish tea I may say, and got a fine welcome. By the time we got back we took some time to melt but it was worth it I must say.

I expect you have heard that Sid and Lib have another kiddy and very disappointed it's not a wee girl instead.

We can't believe we're home yet and have just got our bags unpacked. This neighbourhood is running over with cabs and luggage but today's is the last I think for this time.

We all went to the pantomime on Christmas night – it was splendid. I was positively sore laughing. We hope to see the others before the winter is finished. The comic man asked the comic woman why she did not marry. So she said she had a parrot which swore, a chimney that smoked, and a cat which stayed out all night and so didn't really require a man, so you see although you are such superior animals you can be dispensed with evidently.

The proof of our hockey photo was waiting us and is fairly good, not very, but it is difficult get a good one and the light was so bad, it was a frightful long exposure so we all look like grim death.

Em got that book of Sousa's Marches which you have so is now to be heard thundering them from early morn to dewy eve.

Nona and Winkie are coming in this morning to have a gossip over the week's doings, so it's a good thing this epistle is near its end, there won't be much quiet in ten minutes time.

*I never said I found your letters a bother,
merely suspected you found them so – if ever you
do I won't need very much convincing so don't
scruple to say it. Here's Mary's tammie at the
railing so adieu to all quiet.*
Is all forgiven? – Katie.

All was forgiven, for several days later she received a
small parcel. In it was a beautiful bottle of Yardley's
Gardenia. Katie broke the white wax seal on the stopper
and untied the gold bow of ribbon which exactly
matched the perfume. She dabbed the stopper lightly
behind her ears. At that moment, Emma came in. She
stopped on the threshold and sniffed.

'Whatever is that glorious smell?' she asked.

Katie showed her the bottle.

'It's absolutely lovely. You're a lucky wee girl,
Katie, to be given a present like that. I presume it's from
James?'

'Yes. I think it's to show he forgives me.'

Gently she replaced the bottle into it nest of white
velvet, put on the lid and with her finger traced its
flowing script – 'Yardley's Gardenia'.

[Note: Shandon is on the Gareloch. Crieff is many miles
away. The two places named are copied from Katie's
letter of 5.1.05. She also mentions that Crieff is about
20 miles away from where they were staying.]

11

Following their misunderstanding over Christmas and New Year, James consigned all Katie's letters to the dispensary fire. It took them both several months to reach that level of affection and concern for each other that had warmed their meetings and letters of last summer and autumn. They had to find their way back through a cloud of mistrust and the sad fact that what has been written cannot be unwritten.

However when April came, there was no more need for a daily fire in the dispensary and James began to write from his attic room again and to tuck letters and bills into the Elliman's box.

Once more their letters became informal and chatty. James had laughed at the new hat styles which had appeared in his mother's magazine and mentioned them to Katie, and she wrote about a catastrophe with one of her own hats. She replied:

Murcia
Tuesday 3rd

Dear James,

Wasn't I just amused at your descriptions, I should think I was. I quite agree with you, the up to date hats are simply hideous at least for my style of beauty. You see I am too cheeky looking to wear a cheeky hat, that's the difficulty. So Mother Hocking has so much of Mother Eve in her to be getting books on such superfluities, I was surprised.

The hat which broke up the party is not quite defunct and it is being done up a bit but father insists on my having a new one – says he commands, and one's duty is to one's parent, isn't it?

I got the second prize at whist last night – a nice pair of gloves, wasn't it very lucky? I don't as a rule have any luck at cards. It was very enjoyable – played whist till ten, then danced till twelve and of course I was much taken up with myself.

I am going to ask your advice medicinally. I have a wee touch of eczema on my hand and what should I put on it to get it away? It's not much but it doesn't look very nice, and what you don't know isn't worth knowing. I've always intended asking Dr Camaning but he's out when I am there or vice versa.

Had a note from Meg. She's baked 230 cakes – imagine! Why, a beast of burden isn't in it. The wretched bazaar is in June it seems so I must begin something. Meg says they may be home about the 23rd of June. Emma says that may and may not be very suitable but there's no hurry for a little. [Here follows several ink blots on the paper] *Those are not tears but blots in which you see that my usual tidiness has forsaken me – it's terrible, there's another.*

Father's in great spirits since his return and is not meditating leading a fascinating widow to the altar. He was telling us about a man who didn't get his glass of an evening because his wife objected, so the bailie delivered himself of some unromantic notions, said he'd like to see the wife who'd keep him in like that, and that he'd not

111

change his grog for the best, so we may fear no evil we think.

He's brought home some Harrogate haddocks like whales and we have to consume them, it's no joke, but luckily they are quite bearable. We're very generous with them to friends and keep not all the good to ourselves.

What a day we've had. I was sitting in the garden basking in tropical heat – long may it continue. But I am not reduced to the weather yet.

I've been such an idiot. I had a pretty little pair of earrings, so imagined I might look tricky if I wore them and sailed into town and got my ears, those little fairy shell like ears of mine – pierced and that wasn't bad – not very – but of course I wanted them in last night and took out the temporary rings too soon, and I was nearly two hours getting them out this morning and my ears were worse than they were as they were really healing so quickly. Emma chuckled of course and sympathised none and I don't suppose you will either, but vanity has been well rewarded.

Now I guess I've given you a good dose and like the friend who drops in of a morning may become a bit of a nuisance I think that's what you said, so as the sun has set in the East (?) and it's nearly half six I will conclude – what there's left of me anyway.

Wasn't Emma rude? asked me if I was going to get a ring through my nose while I was at it.

Farewell, Katie.

James smiled as he pictured the ring through Katie's nose. It was good to get her cheerful letters again – and it was April. The nights were lighter, so he was able to walk after the family's early supper. He and Edward had always relished the evenings when they were free from school and had left the house with promises to their mother that they would be back in plenty of time to do their homework. James continued their tradition.

The lanes with their high stone hedges, starred with primroses, violets and now emerging foxgloves, were a soothing contrast to the busy shop and the air was clean, rain washed. One evening he picked a bunch of violets from a clump which had spread over the hedge beneath an oak tree. He packed them in damp tissue paper and posted them to Katie. She wrote to say they had arrived in excellent condition and how cheered she was to receive a little bit of Cornwall.

Now he mixed an ointment for her eczema, labelled it and wrote the directions. This he packed and sent. It occurred to him after he had posted the small parcel that she may well have liked chocolates more than ointment, so he chose a box of the best Cadbury's that the sweet shop sold. On the lid was a picture of two yachts racing in a blue sea – would she think of Falmouth?

In his letter, sent by separate post, he reminded Katie that he had promised to get a racquet for her. He was friendly with the owner of the Falmouth ironmongers who ran a good sports department, and knew that he could buy her whatever she wanted.

James' spirits rose as the April days passed. Tennis was about to begin the new season. The grass had been cut – fortunately there was a dry spell, and Mr Wilmer had been up to the club on several afternoons to roll the courts. The club committee held a 'new season' meeting to discuss subscriptions, visitors' fees, club house rules and so on, and agreed that both full members; and 'artisan' members' fees should stay the same as in 1905. He smiled wryly as he included this in his letter, as last year Katie had spent some time examining the club house notice board and had questioned him in detail about the difference between full and artisan members.

He thought Emma had been unsympathetic about poor Katie's ears. Couldn't she have helped Katie take the earrings out? He warned her to watch for any signs of infection.

The letter ended rather abruptly as he could smell his favourite rump steak cooking – a delicious aroma of steak and onions was floating up the stairs – he'd written this one at home.

Murcia
6ᵗʰ April 1906

Dear James

I only intended you to give your advice as to what I should use for my hand, it is really nothing but it annoys me to see it. It is far too good of you to send anything – you must be thinking I am a fairly good angler but I didn't intend to really.

You seem very particular as to who gets into your tennis club – so you 2½d things won't let in the simple 2d, it is mean! Here, we're nothing like that. We know of course in a club that half the people are drips who you wouldn't know out of the club, but it makes no difference so long as they pay – no notice is taken of them – they go their ways and we go ours. Glasgow is certainly not snobby, if you can pay that's the key to anywhere and everywhere.

Had a note from Meg with a bazaar slip. These little fingers must hurry as the 14th and 15th June is early. She says they will likely come north on the 23rd and that will suit us as we expect to be away from the ninth to the 22nd June.

It's awfully decent of you remembering about the racquet. I think if you can get an E.G.M. it will do nicely – 14 oz and the handles are all the same, there is no great difference. It's so good of you keeping me afloat like that.

We go to Rothesay tomorrow for our last (hockey) match. That's at the coast about two hours from here in case your Scotch geography was neglected in your youth.

Emma really isn't unsympathetic, but considered my vanity needed a little opposition and that getting my deserts in this world, I might be a more profitable servant in the future. They are quite better and the storm is past.

We went and saw the Englishmen give the Scotch such a wigging at hockey last Saturday – it was a choice day – but they were beaten from the start. The English were wee and ran like lightning, were smarter on their feet a good deal.

The post has just delivered itself of two parcels and how can I thank you? It is far too good of you. I'll rub on the stuff tonight. It's merely slightly red – and I'm sure it will be cured. When may I apply the chocolates? By the hour or only once a day? They are splendid and I have already made several applications. They are not the usual medicine recommended by chemists I expect.

Sorry to hear that Mother Hocking wasn't so well but hope she is quite herself again. Why were you so late at bus.(iness) that night? I think I'll need to prescribe for you if you wish to linger in this vale of tears any length of time.

I saw there are still some more miners being discovered in those terrible mines. How can they have lived through such awful times? You should be thankful you're living in a quiet and little simple?!! village where accidents are few and far between. They are quite right to demand better pay, it's such a risk.

Now thanks again. I feel quite ashamed when I look at that bottle and when I taste those sweets – Em says it's a great saving to her account.

Goodbye and do justice to the steak.
Katie.

12

Mrs Hocking, indeed, had been unwell. Usually James didn't mention his parents in his letters to Katie, but his mother had had a bad chesty cold in April, which left her feeling very out of sorts, with headaches and a cough that rattled the windows day and night. Of course, a sleepless night meant a lack of energy the following day. She was an exemplary housewife, but now she dragged around the house, resting at frequent intervals.

As the weather warmed, James suggested that both she and his father should have a holiday, perhaps at Grampound with relatives. Mr Hocking thought this an excellent idea, but Mrs Hocking was dismayed. The thought of all the packing, making sure that their clothes were ready and medicines packed – she really ought to buy a new chemise and two petticoats, not to forget new collars for her husband – it all piled up into a frightening list which she hadn't the energy to tackle.

Added to this, the house must be left so that James wouldn't have to do anything except eat and sleep.

At last they got away at the beginning of June, with many adjurations that he must remember to feed the cat, order more coal, not to leave windows open, to be careful with oil lamps and not to leave the doors unlocked while he was out. Harriet, Mrs Hocking's maid, would continue to do the housework. She had been entrusted with a back door key and would cook lunch for James before she left at one o'clock each day, to stay with her parents.

James went with them on the train to Truro station, not wanting them to have the anxiety of crossing to the correct platform for the stopping train to Grampound Road.

'You'll write to us won't you?' she asked. 'We'll want to know that everything is all right, and I particularly want to hear how the bazaar goes. I'm really sorry to miss it.'

'Of course I'll write,' James said, 'and don't you forget to let me know what train you're coming home on, then I can meet you here and help you with your bags.'

The train arrived. James opened a compartment door, helped them in, and stowed their luggage.

'Be quick,' Mrs Hocking said anxiously, 'if you're not careful the train will start and you'll be swept away along with us.'

But that horrid conclusion didn't come about. He kissed his mother on the proffered cheek and shook hands with his father, then leapt down on to the platform.

Mr and Mrs Hocking arrived at Grampound Road on the 11.07 from Truro and were pleased to see that William was waiting in the station yard for them, with the horse and large trap. The porter loaded the baggage, and William was allowed to peck Mrs Hocking on her cheek before shaking hands vigorously with Mr Hocking.

The long drive to the farm through fields of daisies and growing wheat was familiar and comforting and Emma was waiting for them at the gate. She bustled Mrs Hocking up to the spare bedroom and William tramped up with the luggage.

'I'm longing to hear about everybody,' Emma said. 'But you look a bit whisht my dear. Settle yourself in and then come down for dinner. Or would you like a pot of tea up here in the quiet?'

'No, no,' Mrs Hocking was quite decided. 'I'll just wash my hands and face and then I'll come down. And then perhaps we can have a good talk directly?'

Accordingly by the middle of the afternoon, the two ladies walked along the lane towards the river, leaving Mr Hocking in the shaded parlour with a white handkerchief over his eyes.

They reached the bridge and leaned on the parapet, looking down at this tiny tributary of the Fal. It was shady under the trees and the brook flowed rapidly over the stones. The peace of the fields dropping down to the broad river, the sheep and the growing lambs in the Home field, all was simple and homely and brought back the past to Mrs Hocking, the happy days when the boys were young and still very dependent on her.

'They've built those cottages over there, since you came last time,' Emma said. 'There'll be no fields left at the rate they're going. You'd hardly recognise Tregony, they've put up four new houses in the street, and every one taken by foreigners.'

'Foreigners?' echoed Mrs Hocking, aghast.

'Well, one lot's from Truro, another from Lostwithiel and two from somewhere up country.'

Mrs Hocking shook her head.

'Whatever's Cornwall coming to?' she said. 'I must say we get a very mixed lot in Falmouth. From London and Birmingham, they're all taking advantage of the railway. And down they come, four abreast on the pavements and eating in the streets. My poor mother would turn in her grave to see some of them.'

They gazed at the sunny scene before them.

'What about that Scottish maid you said was pestering James?' Florence was keen to get on to the real news.

Mrs Hocking stiffened, pursed her lips and sniffed. 'Well you may ask,' she started balefuly. 'The boy seems to be besotted. Oh, she's got her hooks into him all right. She'll be down again this August I suppose, tripping along the streets in her broderie anglaise and city shoes, making demands on James' time.'

'Why? Doesn't he like her?'

'Like her? He seems mesmerised by her. But no good will come of it, you mark my words.'

'Well, I don't know I'm sure. But it would be nice if he was to settle down with his chosen maid, even if she is Scotch.'

'We'll see.'

They opened a gate into a field path that led back to the farm.

'It's your bazaar soon, isn't it?' Emma asked. 'It's a shame that you're going to miss it.'

'Yes, I'm very sorry not to be there. But really, Emma, I haven't been at all well, what with this chesty cough and my headaches. I was dreading all the work I usually do to get the hall ready.'

'They'll miss you. I know you do ever such a lot. Perhaps it'll make them realise how hard you work.'

They squeezed through a stile into the Home field and reached the orchard.

'Anyhow, the paper'll be here Saturday afternoon and you can catch up all about it.'

'Yes indeed, though Mr Lukey is opening it on the second day this year and I really would have liked to hear him speak.'

Their way led through a gate into the orchard. Tiny apples were already forming and the undersides of the leaves gleamed silver in the breeze.

13

By June tennis was well underway in Falmouth and Glasgow. Mr Wilmer made use of every fine afternoon by rolling the grass courts at the Tennis club, leaving all the dispensing to James.

James was enjoying the unaccustomed freedom while his parents were away, and there was no one to ask what time he would be in or with whom he was playing tennis. He opened the windows and dared to smoke his pipe inside the house. He ate supper after tennis, instead of before as he did when his mother was at home. He sent Katie her new racquet, with which she was delighted, and bought a new one for himself too. He had never really liked his old one, the balance seemed wrong, but the new one was a success. He had many friends at the club, and always a bevy of young ladies, wishing to partner him in mixed doubles.

Then he mislaid his key to the locker at the club, which he shared with Lilian Head, the grocer's daughter, and had borrowed her key until he found his .own. Unfortunately he forgot to return it to her.

BY HAND
High Street
9/6/06

Dear Mr Hocking,
     So sorry to be always bothering you, but I understand you have the key of the locker again, my key. Evidently I am not to be trusted with it.

I would not trouble you now, only you said you would not be going up today. I do not think there will be many there.

I am afraid I should feel glad if it rained hard.

Yours sincerely,
Lilian Head.

The Head's errand boy had brought the note to Wilmer's, parking his heavy bicycle negligently against the shop window.

'Is there a reply sir?'

'No,' said James. 'I'll see about this, thank you.'

The boy ran off and James watched him turn his bicycle with its heavy basket, full of groceries for delivery, and head off into the traffic, wobbling until he gained his balance. Well, Lilian would have to wait for the key until he went home for lunch.

By lunch time the early clouds had dispersed and Lilian's hoped for rain looked very unlikely. He found the key in his blazer pocket and returned to Wilmer's via Market Street, in order to hand it to her on the way.

He liked going into the Head's grocery store. There was an enticing smell compounded of coffee beans, home cooked ham, fresh cheese and butter, with a hint of paraffin and kitchen soap.

Behind the long counter were shelves holding large red tin canisters of tea, the varieties shown on labels of dull gold – Indian, China, Lapsang Souchong, Earl Grey. Coffee beans were ranked alongside in blue canisters. On lower shelves were jars of sweets and a row of spice drawers. Canned peaches, corned beef and sardine tins were arranged in careful pyramids along the counter.

'Afternoon, Mr Head,' he said as the grocer appeared with a basket of eggs. 'Is Lilian in?'

'Just coming down from lunch, James. Can I give her a message?'

But at that moment Lilian appeared, tying her voluminous white shop apron around her. She was a tall, handsome young woman, her back hand the despair of her opponents on the tennis court.

'Sorry Lilian, about the key I mean. I intended to give it back to you last Saturday, and then forgot of course. Here it is.'

Lilian smiled. 'Your head too full of Scots lassies perhaps, James?'

He grinned. 'Possibly – just a little.'

'Well, there's plenty of nice Cornish maids, remember.'

'I know. My mother's always pointing them in my direction!'

They chatted about the forthcoming tournament for a few minutes, weighing up the possibilities of various partnerships for the mixed doubles. But before he left the shop James succumbed to the allure of a delicious ham sitting on its white stand, the cut side pink and the outside covered in golden bread crumbs.

'I'd like a few slices of ham,' he said.

Lilian removed it from the glass case which shielded it from flies and dust and carved several slices, wrapping them in greaseproof paper.

'My supper,' he said, and paid her. 'It's ten past two, I'd better go.'

A letter from his mother was lying on the mat when he went downstairs on Monday morning. Her bold forward sloping writing, tightly controlled, was recognisable instantly. He read it over breakfast. It was the second letter in a week.

Archivora
Philleigh
Grampound Road

Saturday eve.

My dear James,

 When I wrote to you I forgot to say that probably Mr Pawlyn and Mr Lamb would be calling for our quarterly money, as I know the quarterly meeting must be near. Please give it them, or leave it with Miss Lean. If Mr Lamb shouldn't call, perhaps you will be able to give your Father's to Miss Pawlyn, it is 2/6 each.

 So the bazaar is over. I hope they are all pleased. I see the first day's amount was something over £180. I should expect they have reached £400 especially if Mrs Sandry's big sum was counted in the first day's takings. The Mr Lukey who opened it on the second day must be the gentleman Edith Hawke spoke of in her last letter. Have you met him? I should like to see him, so hope he won't have left Falmouth before we return.

 I think we have decided all being well, to come home next Thursday. Then we shall have a day or two to prepare for your aunt's visit. Bessie's heart is slightly better so they hope she will pull through.

 I see Miss Williams of Lansdown Road is dead, it will be very sad for them.

What a change in the weather. Not very nice
for finishing the bazaar was it?
　　I see there are to be ninety ships at Falmouth
tomorrow, a pretty sight in fine weather. I dare
say there will be a great number of spectators.
　　I hope Miss Lean is very comfortable now and
that you are all well and happy.

　　With love to each,
　　I remain,
　　My dear James
　　Your loving mother
　　E.A. Hocking.

He put the letter in his pocket to read again later. It was
clear that despite her being on holiday in delightful
countryside, all his mother's interest lay in Falmouth and
the Wesleyan Church. He suddenly realised what a
wrench it must have been for her to go away and not to
have the enjoyment of the two day bazaar. She had been
unwell too, lacking her usual energy – it was clear to
him now that she would far rather have stayed at home.
She must have read every word of the Falmouth Packet.
If they had a holiday next year he must make sure that it
didn't clash with church events.

　　He had been out early with his camera on Sunday
morning. The day was fine and sunny and an offshore
breeze rippled the water in the harbour and caused the
schooners and cargo vessels out in the Carrick Roads to
rock at their anchors. Closer in the bay many graceful
yachts and the busy quay punts rested quietly in the
harbour.

　　How Katie would have loved this splendid scene.
She, brought up by the Clyde, was fascinated by the

smaller craft, especially the quay punts moving briskly around the harbour. In her frequent walks between Pendennis House and the shop she would dart down Customs House or Fish Strand quay to watch the small boats, and from the new Prince of Wales pier she would gaze across the Carrick Roads to the cargo vessels in the deeper water.

Later James walked to the quays where the Falmouth fishing fleet was packed along the walls, for they never worked on Sundays. He took many photographs and was tempted to go into the shop immediately and develop them, but worshippers at the Wesleyan chapel were already emerging after morning service and so he decided to go home, as Miss Lean who lived next door had invited him to lunch.

A letter from Katie awaited him at the shop on Monday. Once again her father had taken Emma, Katie, Winkie and friend Harry on a cruise, this time to Norway. He envied them; what an eventful and happy life she led. Sometimes he had serious doubts as to whether she could ever settle down to the slower pace of life in Falmouth. If they married, holidays would be infrequent, and cruises out of the question in the first years, until he had worked up the business. He knew by her descriptions of Murcia that it was a large and pleasant house. How would she cope with the terraced house which would be the most he could afford to begin with? He had mentioned some of these uncomfortable questions to her in his last letter. She had not replied. Perhaps he had worded them too severely, or maybe she was busy preparing for the cruise; at any rate, she hadn't written for several weeks, and neither had he.

He noted the crest on the envelope, red on blue – a lion, a Union Jack, and Albion Steamship Co. Ltd.

Steam Yacht. 'Midnight Sun'.

21st June 1906.

Dear James,

I didn't mean to write but I wanted to so am just hoping that whatever made you so nasty has gone past.

What exquisite weather we're having. Everything is simply ideal. You would have liked it I am sure and the people are very nice on the whole. We are just arriving for the coronation and are at anchor almost next to the Royal Yacht; it is a lovely sight as the bay is filled with all the different boats for the occasion.

We had such a wet day in Newcastle – left home in brilliant sunshine but as soon as we crossed the border it got so wet. But next day was as lovely as ever and I was the only one who was a little sea sick, so my boasted pride was humbled in the sight of my friends, but it was nothing to speak of. Did you have good weather for the bazaar? I expect to get a letter from Meg at Bergen next Wednesday telling us about it and I expect she'll just be off now for Glasgow and not a bit huffy after us thinking they'd be annoyed.

Yesterday we landed at Molde and climbed uphill. We reached the snow on the hills. It was funny to be drinking snow in such heat and what a view we had.

There's a good many Americans on board but mostly English people, though Scotland is fairly well represented. One poor man lost his luggage at Newcastle and is feeling awful. A good thing we didn't.

I expect the old folks are back again and you'll be companionless again – no nasty pipe to pollute the old home.

The day we had in Bergen was very fine, but so hot that we spent most of it hunting for an ice cream place and drinking lemon squash, so lost a good many sights that we ought to have seen. Some people climb every rock and seem to see everything that does or doesn't exist in each place. Harry is enjoying it awfully. It's her first trip out of British ground and she is delighted with it all, and Winkie is playing her mandolin and charming everyone. It's never night here and you go to bed in daylight – it is funny. There's generally concerts or whist till ten. Then you just have your camp chair and watch everything till about twelve.

Now I think I will be winding up because I don't even know if you wish to hear so in case of accidents I will be brief. We only get letters once, next Wednesday at Bergen just as we sail for home, so I am hoping you will have written, but if not it's all right. I can't think why you didn't -------------- now goodbye. Katie.

Poor Katie. Well at least he could write when and where he pleased when his mother was away, without parental questions. That evening after tennis he wrote her a long and affectionate letter, directing it to Bergen.

On the mat at the shop next morning lay an envelope addressed to him. Momentarily he thought it was from Katie, the writing was so similar to hers. But is was from Minnie Clark, wife of his friend Jack whom he had known during his examination preparation in London. They were now living at Gravesend, and had become friendly with his cousins who, by chance, lived nearby.

158 Old Rd. West
June 24th 1906
Gravesend.

Dear Mr Hocking,

My husband despairs of getting a letter from you, so I said 'I'll write, perchance where you fail I may succeed.'

But indeed, seriously we should be glad to hear from you and how you and all your affairs are progressing. We are most anxious to know if the bonnie Scottish lass is to see you this summer; we also want to hear how you and Mr Wilmer are progressing and if any decisive steps have yet been taken. To please us then, very much, would be for you to sit down at once and write to us and tell us all about yourself and your doings.

But I am really writing this afternoon to tell you a piece of news. We are going to move! and we are all so delighted. Our new house is in the Kent Rd, the next road to Mrs Penlerick. We shall have a delightful garden, much bigger rooms, and an extra bedroom, so when you next come to Gravesend please note the latter item, for we shall be only too delighted to have you stay with us.

We are hoping to go to our new home tomorrow week - the painters are in the house this week and so soon as they are out we shall go in. We shall very quickly be straight too, I'm sure. We dreaded another winter in this house, it is so draughty.

Jack is keeping well – he gets tired by the end of the afternoon, but the camera is a great boon and he is now most successful and never spoils a plate.

Enid is always talking of you, and wonders when you are coming to Gravesend, she asks me to send you a particularly big kiss.

I hope Mr and Mrs Hocking are all the better for their change. I suppose you will all be at home by this time.

We all send our kindest regards to you. Please give my love to your Mother, and believe me,

Yours sincerely,
Minnie Clarke.

P.S. We move July 2nd. Our new address will be 3 Arthur Villas, Kent Road.

He must write to them this evening. He had intended to write weeks ago, but as the days slipped by the urge to reply had receded. And what was he to write? Nothing definite at all – only that he was in an early stage of negotiation with Mr Wilmer to buy the business, and that he was not committed in any way to "the bonnie Scottish lass."

Steam Yacht 'Midnight Sun'. Newcastle on Tyne.
28th June 1906.

Dear James,
I was glad to get your letter yesterday and to see that there was nothing up. I'm sorry I thought

you hadn't bothered to write when you had – you see I never feel certain and I so often write something that you misunderstand but am very sorry.

Here we are on the North Sea tossing away and K.O. is stretched on her narrow bunk helpless – how are the mighty fallen – every time I tried to dress was fatal so am here till tomorrow when we arrive in Newcastle at six in the morning, where we will get a train home.

It's been a glorious trip with only one fault but am not going to tell you what fault unless some day when you're really good. Our last excursion was to the largest glacier in Europe and we all went up but Em – and we paid dearly for it – it was terrible and getting down was ten times worse than climbing up. Wee Winkie was a true friend as she owned an Alpine stock and made me take it. She trotted up and down in high French heels but she's a wonderful wee soul. I was thankful to get to the bottom.

Yesterday of course was spent in Bergen. Unfortunately it was merely au revoir and not goodbye to some delightful ices we got there, but such is life.

There was a fancy dress dinner last night, just anything made up out of what you had – it was very funny – Winkie went as Two Strings to My Bow; Harry strung a Norwegian bell round her and appeared as the 'Belle of the Boat' – a bit daring for one of her size. Em collected all the roses in the party and went as 'Summer', and I got my Spanish mantilla draped on and made a fine 'Spanish Lady'.

There's very little of the Lady about the seasick creature penning these lines but am living on the hope of dry land soon to come.

I don't think they made very much of their bazaar but if it's what they wanted that's the main point I suppose, and Meg said it poured all Friday – a most unusual thing for Falmouth??

We can't imagine we'll be embracing Meg and T.H. tomorrow sometime – I dare say Nona will be glad to see us back too.

Don't jump up and down and upset your steak at my next remarks, if you indulge in that refreshment in summer as well as winter, but I've been thinking many things in the solemn glory of those mighty mountains and have come to the conclusion that you could easily spend your holiday at Loch Katrine – Having been struck by my photos of our grand scenery it would only be natural that you should visit it and our duty would be to see you weren't bored. Now James, I wish you would consider it. Everyone is so busy at Loch Katrine that that man Hocking would not be much noticed. I really want to see you very badly. I don't think letters are very satisfactory – and you may not be settled for ages so I think you ought to come when you have a decent holiday, and of course the fishing's such an attraction that it passes for an excuse.

However perhaps our friend Wilmer won't let you off just then, but do what you can. There's nothing to hinder you coming as a friend of Emma's and mine, if you wish to come. So please don't write and say you won't. The old folks will be so fit after their holiday they will be able to spare you for a little while and they get you all the other times and I don't.

I got a pair of sleeve links characteristic of the country which I enclose, hoping you will occasionally disfigure your cuffs by wearing them.

Harry sends her respects and is dressing at present for dinner and Winkie sends this photo she took of me driving a wee Norwegian cart. She's made a violent conquest of a middle aged bachelor from Hull, but he's not stylish enough so she takes her heart back with her. I didn't think there was anything special on board – nearly all English people but it takes a lot of folk to make a world.

Now let me know soon about the holiday – do be nice – you can if you like.

Katie.

Hotel in Norway, 1906.
Photo taken by Katie

So his letter had reached Bergen in time, and what a response – this was the best letter from her ever. Despite the seasickness it was full of her good humour and generosity. Life at sea certainly provided fun, if you were well enough to enjoy it. How he would have liked to have seen her at the fancy dress dinner, seen them all in fact. How fortunate it was that the dinner had been when they were in dock, the ship stationary and Katie's equilibrium unimpaired. He wondered what the one fault with the cruise could be? He must remember to ask her when they met again.

He knew she was right, too, about these long absences from each other. They were the main cause of misunderstandings. Sometimes her phraseology baffled him, and only later would he realise that her remarks were intended to be flippant, all part of her character and her sense of humour.

Instead of going straight home, he wandered out onto the Prince of Wales Pier and re-read her letter. Gulls circled overhead and the yachts at anchor bobbed up and down on the water. The longing to take a holiday, to see her and have a break from work was intense. Yes, he'd do it. He'd ask Mr Wilmer for time off, and go, though he knew this could be an awkward time, with the influx of summer visitors. Well, he could but ask.

As he considered it, various snags presented themselves. What would his parents have to say? Quite a lot, he had no doubt. He'd just have to brazen it out. Then another thought struck him – did they have to know he was going to Scotland? He had no need to tell them. But that was too easy. There were the letters. His mother always wrote to her boys when they were away, at least once a week, and his replies would have the incriminating post mark on them. But if – if he pretended that he was going to spend the holiday with

Edward, or at Gravesend, perhaps they would act as go-betweens, sending his mother's letters on to him. Then he could reply, stamp and address the envelope, and include it in a letter to Edward, who would then post it home. Simple really. It would save distress and complaints all round.

The promised cufflinks arrived in a small package two days later. In a lull in dispensing he ran upstairs to his attic and opened it to reveal a Bergen jeweller's box and displayed inside were the links. There was a folded note too.

'Hope you like them. Katie.'

He liked them very much. They were silver, quite heavy for their size, each one engraved with a Norwegian ship with its high prow and stern. A sail billowed and a pennant blew from the mast head. He removed the links he was wearing and threaded the new ones on to his cuffs. They were beautifully made and bore a silver mark. The edges were bevelled and each corner rounded.

James wore them for a week or so before Mrs Hocking noticed them, until at lunch one day he became aware that her gaze was fixed upon his hands. For a few moments he couldn't think why.

'Have I seen those cufflinks before?' she asked.

'Probably not mother. They're quite new.'

'Let me see.'

He held out his hand so that she could see the little ship.

'Very smart. Well made. Silver too. Did you buy them in Fox's?'

'No, a friend gave them to me.'

135

She chewed thoughtfully. He hoped that she might drop the subject, though he knew that was unlikely. Perhaps his father might intervene, but a glance revealed that his mind was far away, following the roads in the Roseland of which he had been a Surveyor for so many years.

'And who is this friend? Someone we know?'

'Yes. You know her mother. Katie sent them to me. She and her family have been on a cruise along the Norwegian fjords.'

There was an ominous silence, broken eventually by his father.

'May I see them?'

He looked at them through the magnifying glass that he kept in one of his waistcoat pockets.

'Well my boy, that's a very handsome present.'

'Yes, I thought so too, father.'

Mrs Hocking clattered her knife and fork on to her plate. Her colour was high and her eyes bulged.

'Quite frankly,' she said, 'I'm surprised at you James. You know well that accepting gifts from that young woman would distress me deeply.' She dabbed her dry eyes with the table napkin. 'I want you to take them off. NOW. At once. It is an insult to me to flaunt those things in front of me.'

'Now, now mother,' said Mr Hocking. 'The boy can wear what he likes, surely? There's no need to upset yourself over such a small matter.'

'I am upset, as you call it, because James is deliberately defying me. As he has chosen to continue making his home with us, he must abide by our wishes.'

There was an uneasy silence. James could hear the grandfather clock ticking in the hall. A pony and cart clip clopped along the terrace. Miss Lean's dog barked.

James folded his napkin and rose.

'I won't have any pudding thank you. I'll get back to the shop.'

14

July brought in an account for James from Walter Gooding for gloves, collars, two shirts and two nightshirts. It also brought toothache in an upper back tooth. Oil of cloves and aspirin did nothing to lessen it. On several nights he dressed and let himself out of the house to roam the quiet streets, with a scarf wrapped round his face to keep the offending molar warm and to try to soothe his left ear which seemed affected also. At first he hoped that whatever had started his tooth trouble would ease, but it was not to be. He considered going to a local dentist, but when he was in London six years ago he had found an excellent young man, who had dealt very effectively with fillings and an extraction. Walking home along Florence Terrace at three o'clock one morning, it dawned on him that visiting the London dentist would be an excellent reason for going up country and staying for a short while with his Penlerick uncle and aunt, and his cousins, and thence to Scotland.

Next morning he broached the subject with Mr Wilmer.

'I know it's quite the wrong time of year sir,' he began, 'but I should very much like to take a holiday, say, in the middle of July.'

'Oh would you?' Mr Wilmer looked up from the label he was writing, and looked startled at what he saw.

'Well my boy,' he said, putting down his pen, 'I must say you don't look up to much. What have you been doing? Burning the midnight oil, I dessay. Well now, let's take a look at the calendar. H'm, mid July should be reasonably quiet – August will be the hectic month.

'Thank you,' James said, 'I'm hoping to see a dentist I know in London and get something done about my toothache.'

'Toothache eh? Devilish little bones, teeth. Had all mine out some years ago. Never regretted it. So you get your dates sorted out and let me know and if I can't manage on my own I'll have to find a locum.'

That's very decent of you,' James said. 'I'll get my plans together and make the dental appointment. I'll let you know as soon as I can. It'll probably be from the twelfth for ten days or so.'

Mrs Hocking's holiday had been good for her. After the days of rest she felt all her old energy return. The house seemed to be in excellent order too. She sniffed the air in the dining and sitting rooms but could detect no sign of tobacco anywhere, and James was no longer wearing the offending cufflinks.

She was very concerned about his toothache, trying to find something to alleviate the pain. She looked through her *'Home Doctor's ABC'* in her copy of Mrs Beeton. James refused her first suggestion – a fomentation of poppy heads to be applied to the cheek, and oil of cloves had already been tried. In fact all he could taste now was the all pervasive clove.

When James told her that he was thinking of a short holiday with their Gravesend relations, she though it a good idea, although she began to worry, as she always did, about her boys taking journeys – accidents, missed trains, sudden illness and other frightening possibilities haunted her until they were safely home again.

'But what about your toothache?' she asked. 'You need to get that seen to before you go anywhere.'

'I'm going to make an appointment with that dentist I went to when I was in London.'

139

She had no objection to that plan.

'But you must be sure to wash your mouth out – four times a day with salt water. London's an awful place for infections,' she continued somewhat inaccurately. 'I'll give you a pound of salt to take with you. Salt and water – that's the best thing when you've had a tooth out. Four times a day.'

'Thank you mother,' he said, 'that's very kind of you.'

As Mr Wilmer was not yet certain if he could let James go on the dates he wanted, he wrote to Katie to say that he might not be able to go up to Scotland on the dates that she'd still be at Loch Katrine. He also parcelled up a jar of Yardley's Cold Cream, beautifully scented, and sent that off too as a small return gift for the cufflinks.

Murcia
3ʳᵈ July 1906

Dear James,

When I arrived home I was much rebuked by seeing your parcel waiting. I am a very bad lot, but having already hoisted the white flag we will draw a veil over my evil ways. Thanks awfully for it and if it beautifies this young woman at some future date it has not lived in vain. I am awfully sorry myself. I didn't think it possible you'd come sooner.

My family seem to think it would be much better for me to go to Falmouth, and T.H. says he'll do the asking so that it makes it much simpler. So I'll just tell them I'll come if I get permission (from Pa) and I expect I will of course. T.H. is really very decent and I feel a brute for making fun of him at times.

Can you give me any idea when you will be having your holiday? – take it as early as you can as I'd like to come about the beginning of August and of course you've got to entertain me or I am not coming.

We're getting a good dose of the bazaar and how T.H. was a great hero – went to Mr and So and So, a vendor of wood and says, "You go to chapel Mr Wood?" "Yes sir," quoth poor Wood. "Well, I wish you to give some wood to build stalls for Wesley." "Very pleased Mr Sandry." Then on to Mr Tintacks and gets the nails to put into the wood. He really is a great treat and diversion. He came into town with us yesterday and Meg wanted him to go away, as she was bent on extravagance of a worldly order, but stay he would and did, and she bought a lovely sable for herself. He says she is only worldly when she sees us, and he does get ratty when we tell him how proud he'll be when she can pass Mrs Gooding in her new fur, not to mention other ladies of the same importance.

Why didn't you tell me you had given your hard earned shillings for my handiwork? I thought the Southern bachelors had enough to do to keep the wolf from the door without such superfluities. I might have made it nicer had I known its destination.

Please don't judge our worldly position by the paper I am employing – we are not so near the end of our funds as this implies. The T.H.s need a deal of running after and I've just a few minutes, but they go on Thursday, so write your next letter to

Invergyle direct and be sure and let me know what your plans are for August.

I left my umbrella in the train – you weren't here to pick it up. It's been very fine here and no rain since we arrived, but I got a new one just in case of a chance shower. Katie.

Mr Wilmer had not decided on what dates he would be prepared to let James go. James was uncertain too, as there was an influx of visitors, arriving earlier in the season than he remembered in other years. He replied cautiously to Katie, explaining that he might not be able to get away. His toothache was worsening and he felt quite ill with the pain and the sleepless nights.

Then a telegram from Katie arrived at the shop. *'Come if you can,'* it read, *'will be delighted to see you. K.O.C.'*

That decided him. He caught Mr Wilmer just as he was going up to the club to roll the courts.

'Before you go, Mr Wilmer, may I just check with you what you've decided about my holiday?'

'Certainly you may. You need to be off to get that tooth out or you'll have an abscess under it.'

'I think I have already. May I go on the 12th? Then I can make my dental appointment for the afternoon of the twelfth, or on the thirteenth. The sooner the better, I'm afraid.'

'Let's say from the twelfth then. And I'd like you back by the 23rd or 24th.'

James was very pleased. The dates should tie in well – a day in London for the tooth, perhaps two nights at Gravesend, and up to Scotland on the early train, changing at Glasgow. He should be checking in the hotel at Stronachlacher on the evening of the 14th, with any luck.

Monday morning, the seventh, brought another letter from Katie – so they were already there on holiday.

Invergyle House.
Stronachlachar

Saturday

Dear James

Were you astonished at my wire? I thought from your letter that you fancied you could get away in time to take your holiday here, though you had thought you'd be too busy. So if you can come it would be nice. Your previous letter had said so decidedly that it was too late that I gave up all idea of it, but perhaps you have discovered you can come since then.

You'd be far better just to take your full time here, it's too far to come for a week as the journey takes so long. Do let me know soon what you mean to do. We leave here on Tuesday 26th so you have time if you can get away.

Excuse haste but if I miss this post it won't go till Monday. I may have read your letter wrong but I fancied from it that you seemed to wish to get it decided for you, so I just wired as there is so little time.

Katie.

Next day brought a letter, addressed to 3 Wodehouse Terrace, from his cousin in Gravesesend.

[No address
Undated]

Dear James,

We shall be so pleased to see you on Wednesday. Maggie is leaving that day though and I think I have to go to town for the afternoon to see a patient, but have not heard yet if it is to be Tuesday or Wednesday afternoon. I am just waiting to hear from the patient which day will be convenient. If it happens to be Wednesday will you meet our train at Charing X at twelve o'clock?

Then perhaps you could do any business you may have to do and meet us and we'd go home together later? If I have to go on Tuesday I will send you a wire to that effect and then you will be able to come on here as soon as you can on Wednesday morning.

I am in a great hurry to catch the post and I also have to catch the 2.20 train to Farmingham where I have promised to spend a little time today.

Much love, hoping to see you Wednesday –
From
Yours lovingly,
Mabel.

P.S. I called on Mrs Clarke this morning, she is so pleased you are coming.

15

Katie was woken early by the sun, for her bedroom at Invergyle House faced east, looking along the loch and towards Ben Venue in the distance. There was no point in getting up yet, for it was only six o'clock, and yesterday she had finally given up all hope of James coming up to Loch Katrine. He hadn't written either.

Yesterday, she'd taken a lift in the gardener's trap to meet him at Inversnaid, for she was certain that if he was coming, he would be on the evening ferry. But when he wasn't on it, she knew her last hope of seeing him was gone.

Stronachlachar Pier and steamer, 1906
Photo taken by James

Nevertheless she was wide awake now and there was no point in staying in bed a moment longer. She'd dress quickly and go down to the kitchen and beg an early cup of tea from one of the maids.

She opened the curtains and the sunlight streamed in. A low mist hung above the loch, the little islands floating ghost like on the water. Her gaze rested on the jetty and sharpened. A man was standing at the jetty's end. There was something familiar about his dark hair and the way he leaned on the rail looking across the water. It couldn't be? It was.

In three minutes she was dressed, hair plaited at top speed in a single pigtail, face splashed with cold water. She ran down the stairs. The front door was already open and a maid was whitening the step.

'Excuse me.'

The maid was startled, and turned to look after the flying figure of Miss Carswell as she ran towards the jetty.

'James. James. You're here. I'd given up hope ...'

He opened his arms and she darted into them and was enveloped in his embrace.

'Yes, I'm here,' he said, kissing the top of her head.

Then he remembered formality and gently disengaged himself.

'I arrived so late last night that I just took the room they offered me and dropped into bed.'

'And here you are. Is your tooth still aching?'

'No, that's what delayed me. I had it taken out in London.'

'All better now?'

'Completely. I can't tell you how thankful I am.'

'And how long can you stay? A fortnight?'

'No, only a week unfortunately.'

She hid her disappointment.

'A week? Then we must make the most of it.'

She regarded him closely; he looked tired, older than was warranted by the months since she had seen him.

'You're very pale James. You really need more than a week.'

'I know. But I'll soon be all right – up here with you in this lovely place. I know how you've often described it, but to see it, for myself – the loch, the mountains, why, it's wonderful.'

Together they gazed at the calm water and the hills beyond, and at a pair of buzzards circling idly, higher and higher.

'What's the mountain across the loch?'

'Cruinn Bheinn. Quite a modest one really. You'll see Ben Venue later on. It's several hundred feet higher. A real mountain.'

They turned to each other again.

'Are you free this morning? Could we walk by the loch?'

'Of course. Let's meet here after breakfast and we'll go on my favourite walk.'

'Breakfast? Good idea. I've suddenly realised I'm starving,' he said.

'No dinner last night – no wonder. I hear they make very good porridge at the hotel, followed by a huge English breakfast – bacon and eggs and so on. You won't eat that of course, because of your indigestion.'

'Won't eat it? Try and stop me.'

He leaned towards her and kissed her lightly on the forehead.

'I'll be waiting here then. Say, nine thirty?'

Despite Katie's reservations about the wisdom of his eating a large breakfast, he certainly looked all the better for it when they met later. The mist had cleared from the loch and the water rippled now in a slight breeze.

'This is the first really sunny morning since we came.' Katie said. 'But Mr McPherson has just told me that all the signs are for rain later, so we must make the most of it this morning. Oh good, you've brought your camera. Now you can take some snapshots of me.'

'Of you? I had the scenery in mind – views across the loch and so on.'

'Well, if I'm in the centre of the picture, that must surely embellish it? Not just a dull view of mountains flattened out in the snaps as mine always are, but a wee Scots lassie grinning at you. I should have worn my tartan skirt to make it look really authentic.'

They wandered along the path, which led, sometimes through woodland, the trees growing right down to the lochside; sometimes along grassy open places where the sun warmed them. They sat on the branch of a fallen tree and watched the loch steamer 'Rob Roy' making its way towards the jetty at Stronachlachar, the water ruffled in its wake. A sudden movement in the tree above them caught James' eye. It was a red squirrel, closely followed by a second one, playing chasing games along the high branches, bounding lightly from tree to tree, oblivious of the watchers below.

Later, Katie asked him about the progress of the purchase of the shop.

'Slowly,' he said. 'I think Mr Wilmer is in no great hurry. I'm ready now to go ahead, but I think he's intending to complete the sale next year rather than this.'

'But you must find that very frustrating, surely?'

'No, not really. I know it will happen some time in 1907, and I shall have many more responsibilities when it becomes mine, so I'm making the most of my free time now.'

'Yes, you must – it's just that I get so impatient when letter after letter comes from you and you seem to be no farther forward.'

'It will happen. Don't worry.'

They strolled on, only stopping for James to take photographs with his neat new Kodak camera. Katie insisted on taking one of him, with the loch and the distant trees behind him.

'You'd better not show that one to your mother,' she said.

'Don't worry. She won't see any of them. I'll keep them at the shop to gloat over, like an old miser. Anyhow, they don't know I'm up here. They think I'm at Gravesend with my cousins and the Clarkes.'

Her eyes grew round with astonishment.

'James, you never dared. They'll find you out, sure as eggs is eggs. Supposing she writes to you?'

'No she won't. They're all primed at Gravesend. If letters come for me they're posting them right on here to the hotel.'

'But when you reply, there'll be the postmark.'

'No there won't. I've arranged that. I shall write to mother and father, put the letter in an envelope stamped and addressed to 3 Wodehouse Terrace, and put that in a large envelope addressed to Gravesend. They'll take out <u>my</u> letter and post it – no harm done to anyone.'

Katie pictured this for a few moments and began to laugh until tears ran down her cheeks and James had to lend her his handkerchief to stem the flow.

'I never thought you could be so devious,' she said at last when she could speak again. 'And involving others in your unprincipled ways. Well really, Mr Hocking, I feel quite ashamed of you.'

He looked quite unabashed.

'Edward knows too. I wrote to him and he promised to be a go-between if needs be. Oh, you've no reason to look so shocked Katie, Edward and I have had to take evasive action for years.'

She handed back his damp handkerchief, and leaned forward and kissed him. She was gratified by his response.

'Come on,' she said. 'We'll have to hurry back now for lunch – one o'clock at Invergyle House. Pa was out fishing early this morning and he's a great one for punctuality, especially when he's hungry – and fishing makes him ravenous.'

They walked back quickly.

'Ten minutes to one,' James said. 'Just time to wash your hands. What about this afternoon?'

'Come and have tea at Invergyle House. It's all right, don't look so alarmed. Pa will be off with his Water Board cronies, so there'll only be Em and me and perhaps Meg and T.H. They're up here you know, but I think they're going home soon. I'll tell them about your awful deception if you like, then they'll know not to spill the beans in Falmouth.'

'What time then?'

'Oh, about half past three? Em'll be pleased. She's longing to meet you.'

The dining room at the hotel proved very lively at lunch time. At breakfast there had been only a family of four, but now the room was teeming with men – hearty men with loud laughter and cheerful conversation. It didn't take long for James to realise that they were fishermen who had been out on the rivers and streams that fed the loch, or on the loch side itself, and each man was keen to tell his story of the morning's catch.

Two of them joined him at his table and Brown Windsor soup was swallowed to the accompaniment of the tale of reeling in of an exceptionally large trout.

'Have you come for the fishing?' asked the older man, who had introduced himself as John Stirling.

'Well no. I've come to meet a friend who is staying at Invergyle House.

'So you've no interest in fishing then?'

'Actually I have,' James said, 'But not on this holiday. I'm only here for a week, and hadn't planned to do any.'

'Well, if you decide to come out one morning, you can hire all the gear here, at the hotel.'

They ate bread, ham and cheese amid conversation about five a.m. starts, the peace of the loch side, the excellence of the whisky that Mr Ferguson provided and fishing flies.

'Thing is,' said the younger man, 'The manufacturer of the best fishing flies in the kingdom is staying at present at Invergyle House – Mr Carswell, from Glasgow. He's very generous and brings a quantity of flies with him, both for those at Invergyle and for us here at the hotel – it's very kind of him.'

James joined them in coffee and then left them to their wee drams of whisky, going outside by the garden door. There was no real garden here, however. A low stone wall divided the rough grass of the hotel lawn from the equally rough grass beyond. He opened the garden gate onto a lane, little more than a track, and strolled along among the trees which shaded him from the hot sun. Feeling drowsy, he found a large and convenient boulder which provided a comfortable seat. He was deeply asleep within minutes.

He woke some time later and glanced at his watch – three fifteen – time to be returning. He sat there for a minute longer, slowly realising that he felt different, relaxed yet with new energy. His jaw no longer felt bruised. He marvelled that in less than a day up here he felt so much better. Through the trees he glimpsed the loch and the mountain. What had Katie called it?

151

Cruinn something; he'd look it up on the map in the hotel lobby. Beyond the loch were ranged mountains as far as he could see. Then, remembering the time, he knew he'd be late if he stayed longer.

Invergyle House was large and approached by a drive which wound between rhododendron bushes to reveal its many windows. It was built on a small peninsula so that three sides looked out upon the loch. The drive led to a circular carriage turn before a magnificent oak door, but James was spared the need to knock by the arrival of Katie.

'We've a tea table ready on the back lawn,' she greeted him, smiling up at him so endearingly that he cupped his hands round her cheeks and kissed her.

'Beware,' she said, 'This house has many eyes.'

He laughed and she led the way round the side of the house, past flower beds and shrub roses.

'There's only Meg and Emma. T.H. has become obsessed with fishing and is determined to pull a record breaking trout of the water, so he's not here.'

The table was placed in the dappled shade of a silver birch, close to the loch. He recognised Meg of course, sitting there with her usual calm air, her face alight with kindness.

'Well, well, well,' she greeted him, 'Another absconder from Falmouth. How good to see you.'

'Yes, Katie described Loch Katrine so enticingly I had to come to see for myself. What wonderful country it is.'

Katie took his arm and drew him towards Emma.

'Emma, here's James; James, my sister Emma.'

'How do you do?' Emma said. 'I've heard so much about you from Katie that I hardly think you can live up to her picture of you – according to her you're the paragon of all the virtues.'

He laughed and noticed Katie's embarrassed glance towards her sister.

'And you, I gather, are the practical one,' he replied.

A housemaid appeared with a tray of crockery and cutlery, a tea pot and hot water jug. A younger girl followed her with a plate of sandwiches and a sponge cake. In the interval of them setting out the table, he was able to observe Emma. She had the same dark hair as Katie, but she seemed quieter, plumper, helping the maids with cups and saucers, asking about the milk jug which they had forgotten.

**Emma (left) and Katie (right)
having tea in the Garden, 1906**
Photo taken by James

'Your turn to pour the tea,' Meg said to Emma. 'How long are you staying James? Do sit down. I can't keep looking up to you.'

'For a few more days, but I've promised Mr Wilmer I'll be back before the bulk of the visitors arrive.'

'And is Katie planning that you walk to Loch Achray? It's a lovely place. The Trossachs are never to be forgotten.'

'I think she's planning something of the kind. We both like walking.'

'Yes. It's a chance to talk about everything and anything. Tom and I used to walk a great deal; it can sort out many differences and misunderstandings.'

James glanced up at her. She was regarding him steadily.

'You're right,' he said. 'Two spoken sentences can sort out what would take a couple of pages in a letter.'

Katie was handing round the tea and offering sandwiches. She settled in a basket chair next to James and bit into her cucumber sandwich.

'Did I hear you say Loch Achray, Meg? I thought it would be fun to go down on the morning steamer – walk and then return with Archie on the evening milk cart.'

'The milk cart?' Emma asked. 'You'll be jolted to pieces – all that way. And if you'd listened, Katie, you'd have heard me say that they're running an evening trip on *Rob Roy* tomorrow and twice a week until the end of the season.

'Better and better,' Katie said. 'We'd be back in time for late dinner. How about it Jim?'

'It sounds a grand idea.'

'Then that's settled.'

Listening to the three sisters, James was fascinated to find that turns of phrase and little gestures that he had thought were unique to Katie, were shared by all of them, and yet their personalities were very different. Meg, so much older, was plump and placid; her voice was low and musical. Emma seemed to be quiet and practical. She was very similar in looks to Katie, but lacked her liveliness. Every passing thought of Katie's was mirrored on her face.

'Have you brought your camera?' she asked now.

'I have it here.'

He took it from his pocket and they gathered round him to examine it.

'Will you take one of all of us together?' Meg asked.

'Of course.'

Chairs were re-arranged to accommodate the little group. Hats were tilted against the sun and the camera clicked.

It was to be a photograph which James kept – the tea table on the lawn and the sisters gathered companionably. It was to remind him always of a happy afternoon when the sun shone and he was carried along by their light chatter and laughter, as if their happiness was to last for ever.

It rained overnight and when James woke he could hear a steady pattering on the leaves. The clean scent of pine and grass, released by the rain, came in at his open window. He had slept well, better than for many weeks.

He decided to reply to Mabel's letter before breakfast. She was a good sort, his cousin Mabel and expert at her work as a midwife and monthly nurse. Her good nature and cheerful demeanour must inspire her patients' trust. Many of her calls nowadays were for return visits to the same families when another baby was expected.

She and her sister Lily had often come to Cornwall to stay with them when they were children. Mabel and Lily's mother ruled her girls with a lighter hand than their mother her boys. His aunt was not so possessive, allowed them to go out to play, trusting them to behave properly. He and Mabel had always got on well, and they still wrote often to each other. He could tell Mabel things that he wouldn't dream of telling his mother – nothing really out of the way, but to tell his mother anything meant full explanations and rigorous questioning. He had told Mabel about Katie of course, and she was genuinely concerned for him. Now he wrote of how Katie had gone to meet him unavailingly at Inversnaid.

When he had finished the letter, he glanced out of the window but the rain was still falling and the sky was low and grey. It didn't bode well for steamer trips and walking. He posted the letter in the letter box on the hall table and went in to breakfast.

The fishing crowd sounded morose, but determined not to let the rain affect their sport. Presently he watched them set out wearing beige rain capes, looking like an army encampment on the move.

His toast and marmalade was interrupted by the dining room maid, with a note from Katie.

Too wet for our excursion today. But I think a shorter tramp by Lock Arklet would be possible. If you think so too, meet me at 10 a.m. by Invergyle gate. K.O.C.

On his way through the hall a few minutes later, he found the morning letters for residents laid out on the table. Glancing through, he saw his mother's familiar hand on one, re-addressed from Gravesend. He took it up to his room.

3 Wodehouse Terrace
Falmouth
15/7/06

My dear James,

We were glad to get your letter yesterday to find you had such a pleasant journey. With so many travellers by road and rail it makes one anxious when anyone in whom you are interested is travelling. You appear to be having a good time both at Jordans and Mr Clarke's.

I wonder if Mrs Clarke has a photo of Enid to part with, I should much like one. I dare say her Father has taken some of her.

We are very quiet. I was glad to see Bonita on Friday. Miss Lean left us yesterday to go to her brother's. Mrs Lean has gone to Plymouth for ten days.

Your father and I went to Chapel this morning. The weather has been close today, I do not feel quite up to ordinary, very languid and tired.

Sorry to hear you tooth was still troubling you. I expect you will have to get it out, before you get real and permanent ease. The sooner you get it done the better.

I have not heard from Edward since he has known you were taking your holiday, perhaps you have.

I heard Mr Anderton's corpse was rested in the Church overnight, with lighted candles, rather Romish I should say. I don't think it helped him through the dark valley if that was the only light he had. Please give my love to your aunt and girls. Is Lily at home?

157

Kind remembrances to the Clarkes and love to yourself.

*From your loving Mother
E A Hocking.*

Phew! James was thankful that he had had the foresight to write to her as from Gravesend, and grateful that Lily had posted it on. He wrote back at once, remember that it would have the double journey. As he had told Katie, he addressed and stamped the envelope to Falmouth and enclosed it in a second, larger envelope which he addressed to Gravesend.

Truth to tell, his mother's letter had made him feel ashamed at the deception. After all, it was only her love and concern for Edward and him that caused her obsessive behaviour towards them. But then he thought of the rumpus there would be if she had known where he had actually spent his holiday. He only hoped that his letter would arrive home before he did.

To save luggage he hadn't brought any rainwear, but was able to borrow a voluminous cape from the hotel rack.

He waited at the gate and was soon joined by Katie in a light brown gabardine coat with a fashionable matching hood. She laughed when she saw James.

'I see you're expecting we'll be benighted and you'll have to pitch a tent,' she said. 'You can be the pole in the middle and I'll just attach the extremities of your cape with tent pegs.

They walked briskly towards Inversnaid, the loch on their left, its ruffled waters pewter against a grey sky. A sharp hailstorm found them on the bare moor so that they hurried back into the shelter of the trees.

'We're having a whist drive at Invergyle this afternoon if the weather isn't any better. Will you come? There's a curate and his brother staying down the road, and they are coming too, so that there should be at least twelve of us.'

So that rainy afternoon was spent in a hilarious game of whist, with a break for tea in the middle. Katie won the wooden spoon for the fewest points scored, and threatened to give all her erstwhile partners a smart slap with it.

'That'll do very nicely for your bottom drawer,' Emma remarked and was promptly hushed by Meg, but James noticed that Katie's cheeks had turned bright pink. He sympathised – how embarrassing one's relations could be.

16

Whilst they were out on their morning's wet walk, a notice had appeared on the hotel board in the hall, and another at Invergyle House, announcing that a small concert would be held that evening at the hotel. Mr Ferguson, the owner, was fortunate in having a large room, grandly named the Ballroom, in his establishment. Dinner was early that evening in both houses. Many of the guests at Invergyle House were coming; Katie tried to persuade Pa to go, but he preferred to stay in the warmth and comfort of the smoking room, with his own friends.

Immediately after dinner, James and the other hotel visitors helped carry the dining chairs into the Ballroom for the audience. The staff rolled back the carpet against one wall, revealing a smooth wooden floor. They sprinkled the floor with chalk and buffed it to make a fine dancing surface.

By seven thirty the concert party from Inversnaid had arrived, attired in kilts, and had brought along their music, a piano accordion, violin, drums and bagpipes, and two men and two women who were to sing. The hotel piano was moved into position beside them.

Katie had saved a seat beside her for James, with T.H., Meg and Emma making up their group. Silence descended as the violinist tuned up, and then the band launched into a resounding rendition of 'Scotland the Brave'. This was followed by a succession of songs and Scottish laments. The group was lively and tuneful and was warmly applauded.

'Now,' announced the violinist, 'Now that we've all warmed up, I wonder if there is anyone who would like to take the stage with us – give us a song?'

The audience immediately looked away to avoid catching the violinist's eye.

'James,' whispered Katie, 'You could. Go on. What about "The White Rose"?'

'I haven't brought any music,' he murmured.

'You can sing without it. Why, when we were at the Fox's …'

'Yes, do sing James,' Meg had heard them and added her persuasion to Katie's.

'Oh, very well,' James said, and stood.

'I haven't brought any music, but I could sing an old Cornish song, 'The White Rose', if you'd like.

The audience clapped and he took his stance near the piano. His clear baritone, of surprising power in one so slim, rose over them. After the second verse the pianist improvised a soft accompaniment. When he had finished, the whole audience and the men in the concert party, applauded wholeheartedly.

An interval followed and the hotel maids brought in the coffee for which there had been no time at dinner. The concert party people retired to the kitchens to be regaled with more powerful stimulants, and returned for the second half of their programme.

This started with a selection of songs by Harry Lauder. Several of the Invergyle ladies looked startled and pursed their lips. Murmurs of the songs being 'Not quite the thing,' and 'Isn't he rather vulgar?' were heard, but the band struck up and away went the singers and everyone forgot their prejudices in the laughter as they proceeded.

'John, John, for the Lord's sake John
Will ye gae and put your trousers on –

You'll only be a laughing stock
If you gae to kirk in your little short frock –
Oh, your kilt, it's not so verra, verra long
And it looks like being a very windy day
So go and put your trousers on.'

Everyone laughed so much at the antics of the concert party that their applause was rather ragged. When it had died away, the violinist stepped forward, and looked towards James.

James smiled.

'I'll try if you like – if I have the backing of my Cornish friends here?'

'Yes. Yes,' called Katie, Meg and T.H.

As he made his way towards the piano again, wondering what on earth he could sing, his ears were full of 'John, John …' and he knew what he'd do. He turned to the audience.

'I'm going to sing about another John – it's an old Cornish song, with old Cornish words. I hope you'll all join in the chorus – *"Jan Knuckey".'*

He looked especially at Katie and Meg and T.H. and began.

Jan Knuckey was a miner bold
as ever went to bal ...

The chorus was faithfully taken up by the trio –

Johnny will you come along now
Or Johnny will you wait for a while-oh?
Come along John with your big boots on –
Johnny will you wait for a while?'

By the third verse the musicians began to accompany him, and all the audience was joining in, voices free and feet thumping the tempo on the floor.

'Encore. Encore,' they called when it was over, and so he followed up with an edited version of 'Lamorna'

I was down in Albert Square,

162

I never shall forget
Her eyes did shine like diamonds
And the evening it was wet-wet-wet ...

This was greeted as rapturously as Jan Knuckey. James retired to his seat again and was rewarded by a pat on the back from T.H. and Katie's shining eyes.

After a short interval, dancing started. The Gay Gordons came first, simple enough for the English among the visitors, who would either know or very soon learn the steps. The men and women who were the singers in the concert party joined in and helped the dances run smoothly. James was startled by the energy of the Scottish, who danced with a freedom unheard of in Falmouth. He was pleased that he knew the Eightsome Reel, but whereas at home the steps were careful and precise, most of the dancers wearing anxious frowns as they wove through the dance, here the girls whirled around gracefully and the men's neat steps belied their strength. The dances sprang from them so naturally they seemed instinctive.

He saw Meg pirouetting around T.H. who stepped at his own pace from one foot to another. The curate was spinning Emma so furiously that her hairpins came loose and her dark hair tumbled onto her shoulders. And here was Katie again, delivered to him by the intricacies of the dance, floating towards him light as a feather.

As reel followed reel the band increased its pace and its volume. Chalk and dust rose from the floor from the pounding of feet, and after a time the steady beat of the drum seemed to James to be part of him – a loud heart beat that throbbed right through him and carried him along with an energy he had never realised that he possessed.

At last, at five to twelve, the band stopped and everyone found hands to clutch for Auld Lang Syne.

Katie found her cape and he walked with her, arm in arm, back to Invergyle House, the other guests of the house party overtaking them in the station wagon.

'Well, what do you think of a Scottish country evening?' Katie asked.

'It was marvellous. I've never enjoyed anything more.'

'And they loved your songs. It was clever of you to think of another "John" song to follow the Harry Lauder one – and they simply loved "Lamorna".'

They stood in the shelter of the shrubs that grew by the front door of the house, reliving the evening and unwilling to part.

'I've just remembered,' Katie said. 'Tomorrow, if it's fine, it's photograph time here.'

'And what exactly is photograph time?'

'Och, we do it every year – it keeps a record of who was here. We all meet at the garden door and take snap shots of the group. Bring your camera James – please? You're easily the best photographer among us.'

James laughed.

'All right, I'll see what I can do.'

They stayed there, glad to be alone and together, until the door opened and a shaft of lamp light beamed upon them.

'Are you there Katie?'

It was Meg's voice, calling softly so as not to disturb those already in bed.

'Yes, I'm here.'

She reached up and kissed him lightly.

'Early tomorrow morning then?' she asked.

'It's tomorrow already. I'll be here.'

'Unless you oversleep after all your exertions.'

She ran up the steps, turned and waved, and the door closed behind her.

When James arrived at Invergyle House next morning he was in time to find an animated crowd on the door steps, jockeying for position so that at least a part of themselves would appear on the resulting pictures.

Katie had pointed out Pa yesterday, a commanding and lively man, sharp featured and upright.

James joined the other photographers, several of whom were positioning their tripods and diving in and out of the black cloth which prevented light getting onto the film. He felt quietly proud of his own camera, on which several people cast envious glances, as he selected several view points for his photographs.

A number of elegant ladies, with their husbands and children grouped themselves on the steps. Nannies stood about waiting to take their charges back to the nursery quarters. James took several shots of the group.

'And now the Carswell family,' announced Pa, in such a voice that James reflected a drum roll and the clash of cymbals would make a suitable introduction.

At last the family with its accompanying husbands and wives settled down, so that he, the curate, the curate's friend and several guests could take their photographs.

Then everyone drifted towards the drawing room where the Sabbath service was to take place. A minister of the Scottish church, on holiday, had agreed to conduct the short service, which consisted of several psalms repeated by everyone, a bible reading and a ten minute sermon.

Immediately afterwards, the double doors opened and the blissful scent of coffee which the maids were carrying in wafted towards them.

James, in conversation with an older man who had been sitting next to him during the service, discovered that he was a pharmacist from Edinburgh. After James told him that he was negotiating to buy the Falmouth shop, Mr Macrae, as he had introduced himself, gave James some useful tips about running the business, including the name of a photography firm which offered very reasonable wholesale terms.

Katie was at his elbow listening to this exchange. When Mr Macrae had crossed the room to speak to someone else, she said:

'Would you like to stay to lunch? It's always a roast on Sundays, then the staff go off and we have cold supper.'

'That would be very good. Thank you.'

'Right. I'll tell cook straight away.'

Trossachs Hotel, Loch Achray, 1906
Photo taken by James

After lunch they set off up the hill behind the hotel, through silver birch and Scots pine trees until they turned and looked back the way they had come. They settled on a boulder and watched as the clouds were pierced by the sun, mirrored on the water below.

On holiday, Loch Katrine, 1906. Pa seated centre.
Photo taken by James

James pointed to the buzzards circling over the loch again, weaving, plunging downwards near the surface of the water then soaring again on their broad brown wings to swing over the hills behind them and away.

'It would be fun to picnic up here,' Katie said. 'I love picnics and somehow I always get hungrier than I do at home.'

'When you come to Falmouth again, we'll take a picnic along the cliff path towards Maenporth. On fine days the view is splendid. Do you think you'll manage to come to Falmouth this year?'

'I really don't know. I'd like to go in September or October – it helps shorten the winter. But it all depends on Pa, really. The later it gets in the year the less he likes us to go anywhere. Says he can't understand what the attraction is when the days are getting shorter. And I can't really tell him what the chief attraction is, can I?'

'Well you could. I'd really like you to introduce me to him. I feel uneasy skulking around pretending I don't know who he is. Unless, of course, you're ashamed of me?'

'Ashamed of you? I'm very proud of you. I'll introduce you as soon as we get in. But, now you've done the journey up to Glasgow, you know it's not too bad. And I was wondering, could you come up for Christmas?'

James' first thought was the dismay it would cause at home if he proposed to be away over Christmas, and remembered the work in the shop as the holiday approached.

'I don't think Christmas is very likely, Katie. Half the population will have the flu and the other half will be trawling our shelves for last minute Christmas presents. But you never know. It could turn out to be quiet by that time, then I could get the first possible train up to Glasgow.

'That would be lovely – it would be such fun, and I know Nona and Bill would like you to stay with them.'

'Well, we'll see. And by the way, I've been meaning to give you this.'

He took his arm from her shoulders and produced a small box from his pocket.

'Oh,' she said, and then 'Oh' again as she opened the box. Inside was a bottle of perfume resting on a white velvet pad. On the label was printed – Yardley, London. Lily of the Valley. She unscrewed the tiny gold stopper and sniffed.

'Jimmy, my absolute favourite.'

He leaned forward, took the bottle, tipping some perfume onto his forefinger, and touched lightly on the inside of her wrists. He handed back the bottle and she dabbed a little behind each ear.

'For you,' he said 'Because you always remind me of lilies of the valley in your white broderie dresses and those damned cartwheel hats.'

'Damned?'

'Only because a man can't get under them.'

She laughed and unpinned today's Sunday creation.

'There then,' she said, and the flower scent rose between them as it warmed on her skin. He leaned forward and took her in his arms. The perfume bottle, forgotten, tilted onto his jacket as he kissed her. He drew back a little, loving her clear skin, her shining eyes.

'Katie, I love you.'

'Oh Jimmy. I love you so much.'

'Then will you marry me?'

'Of course I will.'

They stayed close in each other's arms, aware only of their supreme happiness.

Eventually he said, 'I must ask your father's permission.'

'Yes, I suppose you must.'

Later, as they walked back to the loch side, she said,

'Will you have dinner with us tonight? Pa will be there and I promise I'll introduce you.'

But that was not to be. No sooner had they opened the door than Emma came running down the stairs towards them.

'Guess what,' she said. 'Pa's had to go home. Some problem in the factory.'

17

Wednesday – and James' last full day at Stronachlachar. He and Katie had decided that they would climb the wandering stony path towards the rocky summit of Ben A'an. It rose before them through green bracken and silver birch trees, up and up, until Katie called a halt.

They sat together sharing the chocolate that James had brought and gazed along the splendid length of Loch Katrine. Little tree covered islands studded the loch which widened into a vista of translucent blue water, small wooded peninsulas reaching out into the sweeping curve of the water. Stronachlachar was just visible on the far bend. The air sparkled and the sun struck across the loch until it was hidden again by clouds.

Then, down to their left, they saw the little steam ship making its dignified way from the Trossachs jetty on its daily trip along the loch. They could see passengers on the deck as it passed below them. On the opposite bank, walkers were taking the waterside path beneath the sheltering canopy of trees.

They set off again, ever higher, until James suggested that they stopped for their picnic, which he had been carrying in a haversack on his back and which seemed to be heavier with every passing minute. From the huge boulder which conveniently provided a seat and a surface to spread out the food, they could see mountains and purple valleys receding into the far distance.

Perhaps more importantly, for it was one o'clock, the Invergyle House picnic consisted of delicious food – Scotch eggs, ham sandwiches, beef patties and generous slices of fruit cake. There was a flask of soup and a bottle of blackberry cordial, beakers, plates and cutlery.

'You must eat at least half,' James said. 'I don't want to carry your share of the food all the way down again.'

Afterwards they leaned against the boulder, sheltered from the chill breeze by the rocks around them.

Katie sighed.

'I wish we could be together like this more often,' she said. 'But I'll definitely come down to Falmouth in the next month or two. Otherwise it'll be a long, long winter.'

'Yes, do come. And I promise I'll ask mother to invite you to tea so that she can see you're not the kind of girl she makes you out to be.'

Katie's finger traced a line of white felspar crystals in the granite beside her, but now she looked up.

'If I do come to tea, I promise you now I won't give you cause for alarm. I'll try to ignore any of her less friendly remarks. I want them to like me Jimmy, and I know it's very important to you. Well, it is to me, too.'

He turned towards her. Her eyes were closed now against the sun. She looked so young, so vulnerable that he feared that she would never be able to withstand the hostile attitude of his mother; and that would probably never change.

'Father will be there too, remember,' he said, 'and he's quite taken with you, you know.'

She opened her eyes.

'Och, he's a dear old boy when your mother's not about. I think he'd be quite fond of me, given the chance.'

Later, they walked back to the hotel, hoping for a much needed cup of tea.

James glanced at the incoming letters on the hall table, neatly laid out in alphabetical order.

171

'Oh,' he said, 'there's a post card – I think from my brother Edward.

Dunstable, Beds.
19/7/06

Glad to get your letter on Monday. I had an idea that you might be north, but I had not heard that you were. Please let me know by wire tomorrow which train you will catch, the 3 p.m. or 9.45 p.m. I would prefer the first, but don't really mind which it is, you can suit yourself. Also let me know what class you are travelling, and if there will be any tennis at Falmouth this year. Don't forget to let me know by tomorrow evening, as if we go by the afternoon train I shall not go back to the house after nine o'clock on Friday.
 Edward.

He passed the card to Katie.

'How strange that although you hadn't told him, he knows you are in Scotland and **also** that you intend to leave London on Friday.'

'Yes, we've had several experiences like that, all through our lives, particularly when we were younger. It's probably because we were together so much and not encouraged to be with other boys.'

'How interesting. And what train will you hope to catch from London?'

'If I leave after lunch tomorrow, I'll get the night train from Glasgow, so I'll have plenty of time to get to Paddington for the three p.m. and meet Edward there. It's obviously the train he'd prefer.'

Two tears slid down Katie's face.

'I can't believe you're going. It's been such a wonderful time. Couldn't you stay just for a few days more?'

'No, I can't really. Perhaps next year? I could maybe get a locum in to look after the dispensing side of things.'

'Then I'll just pin my hopes on coming down to see you as soon as I possibly can.'

When Katie woke next morning, she couldn't remember what day it was – but there was a sense of foreboding. Then she realised the cause. Jimmy was leaving today. Jimmy – she loved the informality of the name and the fact that he hadn't objected when she first tried it out. Now the use of it made her feel closer to him, using a name that no one else had ever called him. She wondered if his mother had ever called him Jimmy when he was a little boy, but decided she did not – she would have used his full name, just as Jim always referred to his brother Edward, never Ed or Ted which might have been thought more usual between brothers.

How were they going to spend the morning? Yes, they'd take the walk he so enjoyed towards the head of the loch. But that was hours away for of course there was breakfast first; and then she had a brilliant idea, she'd go to the hotel and have breakfast with him. That would be a surprise, and would give them a whole extra hour together.

She dressed in her green cotton skirt and her best shirtwaister. Usually she kept it for special occasions but today she'd wear it. It was a fine white lawn trimmed with crisp broderie anglaise on collar, button band and cuffs. She added her green leather belt, pulled to its tightest hole, and surveyed herself in the mirror,

173

hoping that Jim would approve the effect. She added generous splashes of lily of the valley as a final touch. She picked up the little book she'd bought in the stationery shop in Callander – eight engraved views of the Trossachs and Loch Katrine, and set forth.

The dining room maid at the hotel looked a little surprised to find Mr Hocking's posh young lady at the garden door.

'Tell me, where does Mr Hocking sit?'

'By the window over there miss.'

'I've come to have breakfast with him, so would you please lay another place?'

She sat at his table, placing her chair where she had a good view of the door. She didn't have long to wait. His start of surprise and delighted smile told her that she hadn't overstepped the mark.

'Good morning Jimmy.'

'Good morning Kitty.'

He sat down and they gazed at each other's fresh morning faces, only to be interrupted by the maid.

'Good morning sir, miss,' she said. 'Will it be your usual sir?'

'Yes please. And you Katie?'

'Fruit and baps and marmalade please. Oh, and coffee.'

Breakfasting together was new and very pleasant. James silently approved her elegant skirt and slender waist. For her part, Katie thought how much better he looked for his holiday, and how well his light tweed suit befitted him.

The day proved warm but cloudy as they walked along the path beside the loch, dreading the parting, but full of plans for their next meeting in Falmouth.

They returned to the hotel and had lunch together, and then James paid his bill and collected his luggage. Katie suddenly remembered the little green book of views and gave it to him.

'How lovely,' he said and slipped it into his jacket pocket.

The hotel carriage was drawn up at the front door and the people who were leaving were fussing about their luggage, so that Katie and James could only hold hands and whisper 'Goodbye.'

James climbed into the open carriage and turned to wave to her until a bend in the road hid her from view. He intended to take the night train from Glasgow to London, and Katie had urged him to go to 'Murcia' and have a late tea there before catching the train.

This he did, for he was curious to see exactly where she lived, and to meet Bessie, the maid of whom she had so often spoken. Bessie had been with the family for many years and Katie had often told of her as being like a mother to the younger girls.

From the pavement he gazed up the steps of Murcia to its intimidating front door. It was a substantial house behind its black railings. He pulled the bell and heard its distant ringing somewhere in the house. After a short while the door opened and a kindly looking woman stood before him, dressed in black over which she had tied a crisp white apron. On her head was a cap to match.

'Good afternoon sir,' she said.

James explained who he was and said that Katie had said he might have tea here.

'Come in,' Bessie said, leading the way into a sitting room. 'You sit down here and I'll see what MaryAnne can find for you to eat. Mr Carswell's gone back to Stronachlachar today, so you've missed him. I'm afraid

175

there's nothing very grand in the way of food sir, because Cook and I just have the bare essentials.

'Never mind,' James said. 'I'm sure to find something to eat at the station. I'm sorry to have troubled you.'

'No, no,' said Bessie, who by this time had guessed that this was Miss Katie's young man they were all so curious about. 'Sit yourself down sir, and I'll see what Cook can find.'

Some minutes later, she reappeared with ham sandwiches, tea and some delicious girdle scone which were still warm and fresh.

She waved until the carriage was out of sight, until she could no longer see the oval of his face looking back towards her. She turned away and wandered down to the loch – along the jetty where she'd run to greet him just a bare week ago. The loch rippled under a gentle breeze, the buzzards were overhead, the Scots pines cast their long shadows on the water. But she was bereft; without Jim's delight in the mountains, the loch, the rocky streams, seeing everything anew through his eyes, and their joy in being together, her day seemed pointless.

She wouldn't go back to Invergyle House yet, it would be claustrophobic, so she struck off onto the hill path, walking quickly until she was breathless. She stopped at the boulder where they'd sat together only the other day, high above the loch. Sitting and leaning against the smooth rock she lived through the moments of this week together. He was imprinted on her mind – from the second she saw him leaning on the jetty rail, the pride she'd felt when he'd sung at the concert, clear and competent, listening to the compliments as everyone crowded round to congratulate him, their kisses. Why hadn't she introduced him to Pa on the first day? Pa's

176

approval would have dismissed any lingering doubts. She pictured Pa in Cornwall meeting Mr and Mrs Hocking. Surely they would drop their objections to her? Falmouth – she'd love to live with Jim in one of the terrace houses overlooking the harbour, choosing furniture with him, a trip to Liberty's perhaps to choose curtains. Meg would be just down the road, gentle, understanding, always helpful. And she would be with him, no more endless letters, mistaking meanings in the words they wrote.

When James had found a window seat he stowed his luggage on the rack and settled down to watch the endless railway lines branching and crossing, the warehouses, cranes and sluggish water, until the train reached open country and gathered speed. The rhythm of the wheels and the lifting and dipping of the wires on their telegraph poles made a monotonous and soothing background to his thoughts – Katie, laughing, running towards him, leaning over a stream to cool her hands, a kaleidoscope of Katie. Her temper was like quicksilver, come and gone again in an instant – her brown skirt, her green plaid skirt, the hood covering her hair, framing her vivid face. Her hair – he'd pulled it out of its plait only this morning after she'd hurried to breakfast with him. It had rippled over her shoulders in all the wealth of its chestnut waves, silk through his fingers, warm and vibrant.

He loved her. He couldn't understand why his mother had taken such a violent dislike to her. But deep down he had always known that no one would be good enough for him in his mother's eyes.

But Katie – he tried to see them married and living in one of the houses along a terrace – she would make it lovely, for she had a quick eye for colour and design.

Meg would be near, always ready to advise and support her – later perhaps, babies to calm her restless ways, taking her into a realm of selflessness that she, and he, had never known.

These images faded before reality, which he knew could be very different. He'd be continuing with the help he gave at home, more each year as his parents aged. His father now was frail. How Katie would resent the time he had to give them.

As the minutes ticked away into hours and the train thundered through the North country and the Midland plains, he dozed and dreamed of the loch and Katie, until they reached the echoing, clanging, steaming London platform.

18

Invergyle House
Stronachlachar
Glasgow

Saturday.

My dearest Jim,

Enclosed find a letter the hotel people gave us which arrived for you from some unknown fairy across the border –I daresay it's a good thing it's not openable? How I am missing you – and I do bear the weather a grudge. It is simply glorious today and for the first time I need to get into the shelter of my panama.

I needn't ask if you fed well at Murcia having seen you packing pretty fair for one of your size. I've sent this letter on at once.

I want to send you that Scotch song of Harry Lauder's you fancied here. Will you tell me what key to get it in as it may as well be the right thing and it would be nice for you to have a song I'd given you.

Goodbye dear
Your disconsolate
Kitty

[several blots] *It's the nib not <u>emotion</u> which makes the writing so impossible. Tell Edward your brother to be good to you.*

James smiled at this typical missive, and opened the enclosed envelope. He'd arrived early at the shop on Monday, and this small pile of letters awaited him. The letter was from his cousin Mabel.

Riverside House
South Darenth

July 19.06

Dear James

I received your letter yesterday forwarded to me from home. I was sent for on Monday morning, came here by the ten a.m. train, and about ten at night we finished our work, so we were able to settle down very comfortably for the night with a big bouncing boy in the cot. We are going along very well so far.

I am glad you are having such a nice time, and hope it has not poured with rain today, as it has done here. The change will be sure to do you good, and I hope the results of your visit will be as satisfactory as you could wish.

I very much enjoyed the little time you spent with us, it had only one fault, that it was too short. When are you going back to Gravesend? I shall be so sorry I shall not be there to see you, but I know you will be able to enjoy yourself pretty well between our house and the Clarkes.

I suppose Katie was disappointed at not meeting you at Inversnaid, but I expect she would forget her disappointment later on.

I am awfully sorry not to be able to see you if you should return to Gravesend.

I am awfully busy. Much love, hoping to hear from you again shortly.
I am dear James
Yours lovingly
Mabel.

There followed, a day or so later, a letter to Wodehouse Terrace from Mr A.G. Sutton, a sales representative. Having read it, James removed it to the safety of his box in the shop attic.

Telephone No. 207

The Wessex Hotel, Two minutes from railway station
Gloucester

July 24 1906

Dear Mr Hocking,
I am glad you received the Perfume safely for the wife, and I hope she enjoyed her visit to Norway. That is just where I should like to go.
With regard to that little Bazaar matter, I took it up with the Company and they said I could make a refund, so I enclose you 4 shillings which will make the business a little lighter for you.
I hope you are keeping well and that business is good.
With kind regards
I am Yours Sincerely

181

A.G. Sutton
'Erasmic'

P.S.   I intended sending this up earlier as the
Company replied that I could do so a long time
since.

A reply to another of James' complaints arrived at the
shop at the end of the month, on writing paper sporting
an artist's impression of a huge factory in Bristol,
Ropewalk Rubber Works, St Paul's Bristol.   The letter
was typed.

Anderson's Bristol Rubber Company
(Waterproofers, India Rubber and Oil Skin
Manufacturers)
Nosredna Reg.trade mark

July 26 06
Dear Sirs,
    We have heard from our Mr Sheppard that
some of the 'Nosredna' tennis balls supplied to you
have not been quite satisfactory.   If you will kindly
return these to us we will see what can be done in
the matter.
    Reference W H S 31.
    Yours truly
    [signature illegible]
    Anderson's Bristol Rubber Compy. Ltd.

Lastly, in this busy July, came a letter from Katie.

Murcia.
Pollokshields
Wednesday.

My dearest Jim,

Just got back today, though we intended coming yesterday and got the first good day since you left.

The curate came and stood upon his hands and waved to the pier till the tears streamed down our withered cheeks and obscured the scenery for miles around. Bessie was very sorry there was nothing in the house to regale you with. Mary Ann had not expected visitors. You ought to have had tea on the boat but perhaps a little starvation did you no harm.

I expect you'd be as fidgety as an old bear till Edward your brother presented himself. [while waiting for Edward to catch the 3 p.m. Cornish train].

I see you haven't given him those two days of yours – keep them safe – you've no idea how much good a day or two off in the autumn would do you and he's much better to see a little of mother when he so seldom gets the chance.

After we had packed on Tuesday night at eleven (only yesterday!), as the two lone and elderly maidens were gossiping over the dying cinders, a wee voice came floating over the water singing "Will ye no come back again", and on going to the window we discovered the curate and friend landing at the pier, homeward bound, our lamps their only staff and rod in the darksome night.

The friend is a weird man. I guess he happened into this planet about 1780 along with that coat of yours. The curate looked quite a hero in comparison.

Don't you think JIM looks far nicer than JAMES? Your remark about the vacant chair was very neat. I see that association with my superior wit has sharpened yours up to a considerable extent.

I wrote Meg telling her I'd be down in September if that suited her, and think it will be all right.

Now goodnight, be good – and give my respects to Edward your brother and tell him you can't spend any more holidays with him.

With love – Kitty.

19

Work always seems harder after a happy and relaxing holiday and James found it worse than usual, as Mr Wilmer only waited for his return before setting off for his own vacation.

July had brought a record number of visitors to Falmouth, and many of those taking the ferry to St Mawes or Truro called in at Wilmer and Co. for necessities for the voyage, especially aspirin for sun and leisure induced headaches. Pale pink calamine lotion was made up by the gallon to soothe sunburned faces and arms. Kaolin et morph. was always advised for upset stomachs, and dressings for blisters caused by an unusual amount of walking in unaccustomed shoes.

Nevertheless he found time to develop the Stronachlachar group photographs and sent off copies to Katie and Emma.

He and Edward had several evenings of hard play at the tennis club, and while James was at work, Edward pumped up their bicycle tyres and oiled all moving parts ready for a round trip to St Just in Roseland and Gerrans on James' half day.

Edward brought the bicycles down to the shop, so that they could set off immediately at one o'clock. Mrs Hocking had made them two large pasties, still warm from the oven. They took the ferry over to St Mawes.

The day was warm but cloudy. They ate their pasties by a field gate, crushing the camomile flowers growing in the dried ruts of old cart tracks. They were high above St Mawes, overlooking the Carrick Roads.

'The thing I miss most in Dunstable is the shipping.' Edward remarked. 'There's always something on the water to catch your attention – that little boat, for instance.'

They gazed at the boat, whose sails were flapping idly, which was making no noticeable progress along the far coast towards Mylor.

'Does Katie cycle?' he asked a few minutes later as they watched the midday ferry from Truro as it surged down the deep centre channel, packed with passengers, only to disappear behind the cliffs below them and then visible again as it neared the Prince of Wales Pier.

'Not here, but I know she does at home with her sisters. Actually I was thinking of asking her if she'd like to go for a spin when she next comes down. I think Meg has a bike, but if not we can hire one. We could go further afield, out of the way of curious eyes and twitching curtains.'

'Not really?' asked Edward, 'Surely not twitching curtains?'

'You'd be surprised,' James said wrily.

They stopped briefly at St Just in Roseland, but long enough to gaze down on the church nestling by its cove. The air was still, until they disturbed a few rooks momentarily as they circled idly overhead. Then off they rode again, past Trethem Mill until they turned right down the lane and the steep hill, turning right again for Gerrans.

Here a cottage notice board offered "Lemonade and Tea" in wobbly capitals. Lemonade seemed an excellent idea and they sat on the bench outside and drank a glass, before cycling on to the Percuil ferry.

'I seem to remember you two young fellows crossing here before,' said the boatman as they settled their bicycles into the stern of the boat.

'Yes, several times,' James said, 'But we don't get much opportunity these days.'

'Work I suppose,' said the boatman. 'Spoils everything, work do. When I was a nipper we'd be in and out of the river all day long – our mothers didn't rightly know what we got up to – but we'd be off in the morning with a slice of bread and jam, and we'd stay out till we were roaring hungry again at the end of the day.'

'Good days,' Edward said thoughtfully, remembering the times when he and James eluded their mother to help the men on the quay punts, carrying stores onto the boats and off loading them onto the ships who'd ordered them. Sometimes they swam with the other boys off the far quay.

After they had paid the boatman, they set off at speed for St Mawes, to catch the last ferry of the day to Falmouth.

James had received a letter from Katie on Tuesday morning.

Murcia
Sunday Evening.

My dearest Jim,

So you are really working? What a change for you, to be sure, you'll be hoping frère Wilmer won't linger too long holidaying in your parts at that rate.

I am working very hard too, so can sympathise – as I have just learnt to NET and am deep in the depths of many mysteries – quite unknown and undreamed of by long suffering males.

I have no doubt you may see the result before the grass waves over your youthful head.

It never snows but it rains and Bill being away on his holidays, I have go in and do father's

French correspondence for him, and as Frenchies write shockingly it's often impossible to make out a single word, no wonder I'm turning grey – you'd better get that dye into shape so's I may get it when I need it without delay. The people opposite think I am the new type-writer and are very curious – or is it my attractiveness? However, I must not lead you to commit 'flathry' and drag you down from your higher pinnacle so you needn't consider the question mark of any consequence, friend, this time.

We've had such a stirring Sunday. Pa went off to see some American customers – to do the civil, and in came Tommy Reid – clay pipe and other evils. You will remember his little practices without my going into vulgar detail. He astounded us by inviting one of us to go with him as his guest to Dublin at the end of the month, to be present at numerous festivities given to leading lights of the literary world, which was very kind of him – but of course we could not go; neither of us fancy being taken for his wife, but he never thought, as he takes his young nieces with him a good deal. I daresay he thought it was just the same.

Em was delighted with the photo in the waterproofs, it does look savage doesn't it?

I expect Edward "your brother" will be getting near the end of his little outing? Did you get any more fishing? – note please that I don't say more fish – not wishing to induce you to fib more than is necessary.

Now dear, am just going off to snatch a few hours of beauty sleep before the cares of a new day begin so I must conclude with love

Kitty.

Supper was late because of their ride – for Mrs Hocking liked to serve it at six fifteen as soon as James returned from the shop. He stayed up to reply to Katie's letter. He smiled when reading of her work at her father's office, and declared ineptitude at translating from the French. In fact he knew, because Emma had told him, that Katie was a fluent French speaker and the letters she had to deal with, apart from the writing, were easy for her to translate. Katie had once remarked to him that she would have liked to have the task of going down to Pa's office several times a week, to deal with these letters, but of course they were part of Bill's job, and Bill was Nona's husband, and she wouldn't dream of taking some of his office work away from him.

As their ride was fresh in his mind, James' letter was mainly about their trip around the Roseland, the poppies they had seen growing amongst the ripening wheat, the wild roses and honeysuckle on the hedges and the old Percuil boatman.

Katie's reply was prompt.

Murcia
Friday

My dearest Jim,

I didn't know you were given to biking but I expect you'd have a fine ride – the better the day the better the deed, and after having been so attentive at church when North, a little change would do you the world of good.

The two groups are splendid, awfully good, so were the views you sent. There has been no

189

fogging fortunately. I will give you the addresses of the folk [in the group] and you can send them yourself. I'd likely forget or let them stray if you sent them to me to send on; much hot water have I got into with T.H. for not always sending what he sent north, east, south and west.

Cleland, "Bonvil", Maryhill, Glasgow. Primrose. "Redholm"–, Glasgow. Campbell 2 Meadow Place, Kilmorlie. McCall 8 Beaton Road, Maxwell Park, Glasgow, and Emma and I each want a group for our albums, so I trust you have enough to do in the coming bye and bye.

It is very sad about the tiny Cecil. Em had a note from Sidney saying he'd died in his sleep on 9th past – he wasn't really ill, only cross and had a slight cold, and in the morning they found him quite dead. It is very sad for them, and so unexpected. Of course in Africa and India children have very sudden illnesses.

Bessie said yesterday that you'd been very good and behaved quite prettily on the way home. She's got a very long tongue and I can't get out of her what she said and what she didn't say, but the pair of you seem to have said a good deal.

Pa has never said anything about the weary looking stranger at Stronachlachar so I can't say what he thinks or if he thinks anything at all. T.H. is fishing every morning, a nice change for him – and Bill gets notes for different lines and things nearly every day – he seems to have caught the fever very badly.

As you said you were writing again I waited to answer both, but you mustn't bother if you can't manage long ones while Edward your brother is there as you can have no time at all.

190

*The neighbourhood here is quite lively. We were asked to Gareloch tomorrow for a week, but Em is banting [i.e. dieting] and I want to lie low now till later on, so we didn't go, and we are very comfortable here doing as we like. You've to do pretty much what **they** like down there and everything here is looking so nice there's not the same temptation to go away.*

We were up at Nona's last night. When she has a few friends in it's always good fun – though Bill says he's always ashamed of her when she is at her funniest. She goes down to Gareloch tomorrow and Bill gets a week just now so they are quite happy at the prospect.

Now goodbye friend, the best of friends must part. Don't let Edward fill the vacant chair completely –

Yours lovingly – Kitty.

The purchase of the business was progressing at snail's pace and the snail came to a complete stop when Mr Wilmer went on holiday. However, James found time to continue his examination of the books, working out every month's balance between turnover and profit. As the prospect of owning the shop came nearer, he made hopeful plans for smartening up the premises – paint, new signboards, new window fittings, perhaps etched glass doors backing the display shelves in the windows. These would still allow light to enter, and would neatly divide the windows from the shop, cutting down on dusting, and more importantly, theft.

James was so immersed in work and plans that he had almost forgotten his friend Stanley's suggestion of joining him in partnership when his father and father's partner retired. He was surprised therefore to find a letter from Stanley waiting for him on the breakfast table.

'Is that Stanley's writing on the envelope?' Mrs Hocking asked. 'I notice it's come from Newbury.'

'Yes mother, it is.'

'I always know his writing,' she continued. 'Has he anything interesting to say?'

'I'll tell you when I've read it.'

He knew his mother's tactics of old. She always tried to bounce him into reading a letter aloud, straight away, before he'd had a chance to read it himself, and he'd found that he would be reading paragraphs to her containing things he didn't really want her to know. He was wiser now.

Penlee, Newbury
9 Aug. 1906

Dear Jimmy,

It seems a long time since I wrote you, and I expect you will be surprised at getting a letter now.

However, to put it plainly, both Mr M senior and my Pater intend getting out of business before very long and fresh arrangements will have to be made. The first thing that will have to be decided is whether I will enter partnership with H.R.M., and if not should I be prepared to carry on without him. This is a difficult question, as his optical biz brings in the firm a profit of from £250 to £300 per annum – which is not to be lightly thought of.

I was wondering what you were doing now, if you have not a biz and cared to join, I believe it could be worked between the three of us – of course I have only to say the word and H.R.M. would go and Mr M's half would be for sale – or then if not – as I say there would be a fair thing for the three of us, but still I should be glad of your opinion.

    Kind regards from all,
    Yours v. truly
    Stanley Hickman.

P.S. I am going for my holiday on Aug. 24 with John Skinner to Zermatt for a fortnight – will you join us? If so wire me and I will secure a berth for you. (by Dr Lunn and Co.)

Having read through the letter, James read it aloud to his parents.

'Well of course,' his mother said when he had finished, 'There's no question of you joining Stanley now you're so far on with your arrangements with Mr Wilmer, and Newbury's so far away too.'

'There are trains mother. Anyway, it's a generous offer and I'll think about it before refusing altogether.'

'Far better that you should write and refuse immediately. You can't possibly want to live up there.'

At that moment James felt that Newbury would not be far enough away. He would like to wire Stanley today and accept any offer the Hickmans cared to make. Then his father spoke.

'Let the boy decide for himself Ellen. He knows the business, we don't.'

James was silently grateful to his father, who so often stepped in to mediate.

'Though for my part,' his father continued, 'I shall be hoping that you will refuse, James, and go ahead with Mr Wilmer's business. Here, you'll be sole owner remember, able to make all your own decisions.'

'Thank you father. I'll certainly bear that in mind.'

Stanley's letter was followed the next day by one from his father, Mr Hickman senior.

1 Downshire Square
Reading

Aug 13. 1906

Dear Mr Hocking,

Stanley tells me he has written to you re our business which before long will have to undergo some change, and I have seen your letter in reply.

Of course, you know our business is a very good and old one (about 100 yrs) and has been well maintained in spite of the competition of the times – I enclose you a few figures.

With regard to H.R.M. (my partner's son) it would be desirable for some reasons to retain him as a partner if he and his father agreed, as his optical department brings in a profit of £200 a year and could be increased. He has the monopoly almost in this town, and is decidedly clever in it.

Suppose you bought two thirds of Mr M's share it could be worth as things average £500 a year, and if H.R had the other third he could have about £250 (perhaps he might have a commission too?) So I think it would be more worth your while than the offer you have.

If they didn't agree to this, (and it has not yet been mentioned to them) perhaps you might buy all Mr M's half share; the arrangement could be 3, 5 or 7 years.

Stanley is a thoroughly good, conscientious and business like fellow and even if he were not my son there is no one I know whom I would more confidently recommend as a partner than him:

Let me hear from you as soon as you can. I should like your ideas before mentioning it to Mr R.M.

Believe me
Yours very truly
F. Hickman

Within a couple of days James had replied to Stanley's letter, and that from Mr Hickman too. Affairs had not yet gone far enough with Mr Wilmer that he couldn't back out if he wanted to.

An immediate reply came from Stanley.

Penlee, Newbury
Aug 14.06

Dear Jimmy,

Thanks for yours – I was glad to hear you were not fixed up in biz yet, and that there seems a chance of our being able to work things together –

I had a long talk to the Pater on Sunday re the business and he is writing you details of Returns and Profits, as that is more his department.

You will see that if you invested £2,000 in our biz. tt would probably bring you in anything from £500 to £550 profit for your outlay, which is considerably better than the £367's of Mr W's.

If H.R.M. (the partner) wants to stay in the biz. I think it would be advisable to keep him as you see the profit on the Optical Dept. is large and we could keep him in that Dept. together with Photography and we two could run the other part of the show.

The Pater and Mr M are going to talk things over again shortly and directly anything fresh crops up I will at once write to you, although I do not anticipate anything till after my return from my holiday.

As far as I know, it is Mr M's intention to retire in about 12 months' time, and in the event of your coming in, I should say the thing would be for you to come in in about six months' time, so that you would acquire a knowledge of the various Depts before taking the thing over. But if you think favourably of course the thing would be for you to come up and talk matters over, this would be far more satisfactory than heaps of letters.

If you should happen to come in, you can rest assured that you would be going into a sound concern and anybody who knows our biz. would confirm this.

The wife joins me in kind regards, and please remember me to your people very kindly, and with good wishes for yourself.

Believe me,
Yrs truly,
Stanley.

This letter was followed by another, from Stanley's father, some days later. James had spent the interim period considering the possibility of Newbury. It held some great advantages – it was a sound business, he knew that from his visit there to see Stanley again. Newbury would be easier for Katie too. She wouldn't be irritated by the constant presence of Mrs Hocking. He would be responsible, of course, for his part in the business, but that responsibility would be shared with Stanley. Mr Hickman senior, however, wrote on a cooler note than Stanley, and matters were put in perspective.

Reading
Aug. 19 06

Dear Mr Hocking

Thanks for your letter, which I am rather in a fix about answering, for I have sent it for Stanley to read, and forget the points I meant to write about. He will no doubt write to you soon. Of course your name has not been mentioned to Mr M. Senior and I should not care to ask him what he wanted for his half share till he decides something more definite –

*Of course he would like to see H.R.M. in it, but so far he has not been a **partner**.*

The return I gave you included the Optical, but also included salaries which could be re-arranged and reduced by £100 to £150 a year.

If the opportunity offered, do you think you would be disposed to buy it on the lines indicated in my last letter? (n.b. this letter is missing).

Otherwise the Optical could be sacrificed, the capital required would be less, and if it did not work it could be altered.

As soon as I hear anything further I will write to you again.
Believe me,
Yrs faithfully
F. Hickman.

Having read Mr Hickman's letter, and re-read those from Stanley, James decided to let the Wilmer purchase continue on its slow and winding way. If the Hickmans' came up with a firm offer in time, he would think again. In the meantime, he was puzzled and rather annoyed that Mr Wilmer had decided to employ another junior pharmacist. It seems an unnecessary expense and could cause problems when and if James took over the business. He sought Katie's opinion in his next letter.

20

Looking forward to Katie's arrival, James picked up a current timetable from the railway station, and marked on it the train which came from London straight through to Falmouth.

Mrs Hocking had heard that two of her nieces, her sister's youngest girls, were travelling down to stay with the Probus relatives. James wrote his usual Sunday letter to Katie and enclosed the timetable, also suggesting to her that his cousins would be good companions for her on the journey.

The reply came several days later.

Murcia
22ⁿᵈ Aug 1906

My dearest Jim,

Thanks very much for the timetable and I think the 9.50 a.m. is just the one I will take as I see you don't require to change at Truro. I never can be bothered getting my things out – generally leave half of them inside.

It's very sweet of you to think of landing me on to your poor cousins, but please don't say anything to them as I am far too bashful to travel with two unknowns I've never met. You don't believe that thinking I have more than my share of natural impudence – but it's quite true. I'd be in a perfect canary fit so don't say anything to them, like a dear.

Emma has a friend in London town who says it will be a pleasure to meet my train and see me packed into the other one, so that I will be all right, as once inside I'll sleep the sleep of the righteous till I reach Falmouth.

I haven't told Pa that I contemplate leaving his humble roof for pastures new yet, but intend to do so tonight if he seems in a likely humour.

Meg is quite excited and the front door will be opened, not for my worthless person, only royalty and baronets command that, but for my goods and chattels.

We're having a Tennis Tourney running Monday Wednesday and Friday evenings of this week, an old gentleman giving prizes. Everybody plays everybody – and the handicap is hidden so you don't know what you've to give till it's over. I drew a very youthful but a very good partner and we won all our games on Monday, so hope to continue.

You won't have so much to do with another man in the place, looks more like extending than retiring I'm afraid.

Yours, Kitty.

Passing Harvey's on his way back from lunch, James noticed a box of chocolates, the lid depicting a tennis party, the girls in white, the men in striped blazers, all drinking lemonade, their racquets prominently displayed. He went into the shop and bought the box. Tearing a piece of white wrapping paper from the huge roll in the dispensary and racing up the stairs two at a time to his attic he wrote a short note to Katie to send with the chocolates, in which he told her that he intended to write to her father. He asked if he should send a copy of the

200

letter to her first, so that she could approve his wording. After all, it was a terribly important letter and he didn't want to get it wrong. He wished that he might have been introduced to the great man while he was at Stronachlachar when he could have asked him in person, but of course the opportunity had been missed. He smiled when he thought of his proposal to her, and her shy delight – quite unlike the Katie he thought he knew.

Murcia
Tuesday

Dear Jim,

It was too sweet of you sending me those chocolates. I did appreciate them. I like to think you bothered getting them for me.

The Yankee ladies (wife and daughters of one of Pa's customers) leave today for which let us be truly thankful. They are nice, but we are glad to see them go, though they appreciated the sights and we hadn't to force them into our beautiful art gallery like some people you know fairly well.

I didn't get the prize but it went to a nice wee girl so I didn't grudge it to her – our score was the highest but our handicap pulled us down too far to win.

It's a good idea for you to send your letter to Pa to me first then I can see if you put anything daft and probably be able to give some advice. I haven't the faintest notion what Pa will say but anyway I don't think you need worry. Bill said he went up father's office stairs twice before he had the courage to go in, so you haven't that to do , though I must say I wish it over myself somehow.

September is a very jolly month here. All the clubs hold a garden party and couples come from far and near to play for prizes. Ours is Saturday and the neighbourhood dons it bravest garb and comes and watches while it sips tea and ices. I have been asked to play in all of them, so will have a fairly good time.

However, I won't have such a good time when everybody knows as the men prefer to ask girls who are not engaged so I make hay while the sun shines. So I hope you appreciate my permission to allow you to write to Pa as you ought to – such a wee monkey as you are.

We're just going to see our beloved visitors off, may peace go with them and nothing hinder their departure as Em and I have promised to go to tennis to practise for Saturday – you see you hate playing badly as your partner has to pay pretty sweetly to enter – different from our own private little tourneys altogether.

Meg confided how disappointed Tom (T.H.) was with his photos....

Give Edward my respects and tell him not to take you off your favourite stand by the window to lunch as youth is the season for work, not that you know the meaning of the word as I do.

Now thanks James again for your kindness in sending me those sweets, it is very good of you, but here's the cab so I must hasten from the heights of sentiment to the valley of the mundane and say goodbye –

Katie.

P.S.   What will mother say when she hears her "eldest joy" is going straight to the d----?   Don't let this fall out of your pocket please – K.O.C.

This letter didn't remain in James' pocket. He quite agreed with Katie that his mother's wrath would exceed all known bounds. He took it upstairs immediately and stowed it in the box.

September was holiday time for many of James' friends and relations. He had written to his friend Jack at Gravesend, suggesting that he might take the Falmouth bound boat which regularly sailed from the Thames estuary to the West of England.

Some time later James realised that although several weeks had passed, he had had no reply. He was about to write again, when a letter arrived from Jack's wife Minnie.

3 Arthur Villas,
Kent Rd,
Gravesend.

Sept 1ˢᵗ 1906

My dear Mr James,

  I feel I must write to you in reply to the letter which came for Jack, and which I sent on to him. It was so very good of you to have wanted him to come to Falmouth so much, and he wanted to come badly for you know what we both think of your lovely Cornwall, and it was only last Thursday he finally decided not to come. It was really quite funny – first he said he would, then he said he wouldn't. The difficulty was to get him to go away at all.

*The thing that really decided him not to take the trip to Falmouth was the state of the Channel – the week previous we ran across to Boulogne and when we got **into** the channel we were both very ill, especially returning, and all last week the Channel was very rough and unsettled and I got nervous – you know how much my husband is to me. George was staying a few days with us, he had been on one of the Booth line trips to Bordeaux and Biarritz and in returning, off Dover it was very bad and foggy; most of the ladies were very worried. The next day after getting here he went to Herne Bay and almost everyone was ill both going and returning and the river very foggy – so that seemed to quite settle Jack. If George could have come with him, as he would have done could he have returned soon enough, I wouldn't have minded –*

The heat here had been very great and he also felt that possibly Sutton-on-Sea on the Lincolnshire coast where Will and his wife were staying would be more bracing for him.

*But he is coming back tonight – it's been **such** a long week to me. He says he'll never go away again without me – for I think he has missed me too – but I have had a letter each day. There is a model husband for you!*

Please give my love to Mrs Hocking, and I'm sure Enid will want to send hers to her and also to you – she is always looking out for you. When I told her Uncle George was coming she said, "I would much rather it were Mr Hocking coming

because he loves me and kisses me." She is very
funny, but you are a tremendous favourite.

I expect Miss Carswell is with you, or rather at
Falmouth now. I hope she will have a good time.
When you can spare a few minutes please tell us
how you are progressing, and if Mrs Hocking will
be reconciled – I do hope she will, it will be
pleasanter all round.

I didn't mean to write so long a letter, but my
explanation took time. We shall be so pleased
when you can come again to see us. Shall you be
running up to town at all? If so please do get
down as far as Gravesend.

And now it's really time I stopped –
With many thanks for all your kindnesses,
And my kindest regards.
Yours always sincerely
Minnie Clarke.

So, no Jack then this year. Perhaps next year he could
persuade the whole family to come to Cornwall – surely
Minnie and young Enid needed a holiday too?

An envelope written in an unknown hand came from
Newbury. Puzzled, he tore open the envelope to
discover a letter from Stanley, written in pencil.

Penlee,
Newbury.

Sept. 06

Dear Jimmy
Many thanks for your letter – you will doubtless
wonder why this is in pencil. Fact is, I am in bed

205

and booked here for another fortnight. And this is the result of my holiday –

Fact was we overdid it. We went straight to Zermatt from London without any break and then started climbing and on one or two occasions did some very fatiguing climbs – one day climbed up to the Gornergrat which is 10,000 feet up – it was a boiling hot day – took 5 hours up and 3½ back – but did not then experience any ill effects.

We stopped at Zermatt a week (this is 5000 feet up) and I found that I could not sleep at this altitude. Then after that we went another 7000 feet up to the Riffel Alp, where there is a decent hotel and stopped there three or four days, and on one day there we did a big climb and walked over a glacier which was rather fagging.

Felt fairly right till 2 or 3 days after I had been back when I felt beastly rotten – could not make it out, as one day I would be alright and the next like a boiled owl. So yesterday morning I made up my mind all in a hurry to go up and see Jenkins. I thought my throat was going wrong again.

Well he exd my throat and found that alright and then my chest which was quite right and then he came to the heart which was now the cause of the trouble.

He found that it was nearly double the size it ought to be and was going like a sledge hammer. So he called his neighbour Dr in, a heart specialist and they found that I had strained the heart. Of course they wanted to know all about Zermatt and what we had done and the result was that what with no sleep and the climbing and the altitude, that I had altogether overdone it.

So here I am in bed for a fortnight under their orders and I am going up to see them again in about 3 weeks time, when I hope to report more favourably, and so you see my holiday was not quite the success I imagined it was going to be.

Well now, as regards biz – I know not what to tell you at present – of course I cannot move in the matter, but when I am better, no doubt there will be a conflab and immediately there is, I will report progress.

Of course I do not blame you at all for not wanting to go in with HRM, but I thought that perhaps it could be worked.   As regards the Pater's suggestion about the 3,5 and 7 years – he evidently meant it could be terminated at either of these periods. I do not know whether I told you we have a son and heir born last Feby – he is a fine boy and is doing A1 – Mrs H is, I am glad to say, very well.

Joan was not well in this hot weather but is better now and I am the froggy one of the family.

I hope you are well. I forget whether you are engaged to the Scotch lassie or not – you might enlighten me when you write.

I hope your people are well, will you please remember me kindly – The wife joins me in kind regards.

Yrs ever
Stanley Hickman.

James replied immediately, with sympathy and bracing and optimistic words.   Actually, he was alarmed by Stanley's condition which sounded very serious. He had read the major part of the letter to his parents omitting the reference to Katie of course. They had been very concerned. Mrs Hocking remembered several cases in her family where very much the same condition had rendered the sufferers a total invalid. She copied out her recipe for Beef Tea, which she said was very strengthening and easily digestible. James included it with his letter, in which he told Stanley not to worry himself with business affairs – they could be sorted out later, when he had recovered.

Katie arrived early on the Thursday afternoon, in time for a late lunch and a long chat with Meg, who sat, as usual, on the bed while she unpacked her clothes.

'See Meg, I travelled light this time – only two cases and my dressing case!'

'And that weighs a ton, according to T.H.'

'Ah yes, but look what I've brought you.'

She opened one of the cases and took out a parcel, handing it to Meg. She had forgotten how her sister liked to save every little bit of string – 'It's sure to come in handy.' – and waited impatiently whilst Meg untied each knot and rolled the string into a neat ball.

At last Meg pulled off the tissue paper to reveal a silk and cashmere shawl, woven into a Paisley pattern of deep green and cherry red, enlivened with gold silk thread.

'Why, it's absolutely beautiful, Katie. Thank you so much.'

Meg folded the shawl into a triangle, whisked it over her shoulders and admired the effect in the dressing table mirror.

'Do you know, I'm sure this red is the same shade as a pretty winter dress I've been admiring in Gooding's.'

'Good gracious, Meg – don't just admire – have you tried it on?'

'No. I've been trying to persuade myself that I really need another winter dress.'

'Of course you do. I know, it's only half past three. We could go to Gooding's now – you can try it on and I'll give you my opinion.'

Ten minutes later they set out, Meg taking the shawl to see if it really matched the colour of the dress. Upstairs in the Gooding's Ladies Fashions salon, Meg asked about the dress which was not now on any of the plaster models which discreetly advertised the new stock. She was very much afraid that it might have been sold.

'Oh no, the Diana style,' said Mrs Gooding, turning to the young assistant. 'In the stock room, Hattie. Find it quickly.'

Hattie soon returned with the dress, wearing its white cotton dust cover. Mrs Gooding removed it to reveal a lovely dress of silk and wool, cherry red indeed, with a high cream lace collar.

'If you would like to try it, Mrs Sandry,' said Mrs Gooding, 'Please come into the dressing room.'

Katie stayed in the salon and eyed the modelled dresses. They all looked rather matronly; not quite my style yet, she thought. She wished Meg would hurry, for she had important business further along the road in Market Strand.

Meg emerged at last, looking stylish and happy. She had arranged the shawl round her shoulders – the colours the exact match of the dress.

'You must have it, Meg.' Katie said.

'It's lovely isn't it?' Meg said. 'But I don't know what Tom will have to say about it.'

'Och, never mind the dear man,' Katie said. 'When he sees you in it he'll think you're just the best woman in the world.'

Meg beamed.

'Well, you'll have to back me up when he sees it, Katie.'

'I surely will.'

Meg walked to the dressing room pausing to admire the flow of the skirt in the various mirrors. She turned to Katie.

'Don't wait for me Katie. I'm sure you'll want to be off.'

Katie checked her hat in a mirror, pulled back an escaped wisp of hair and ran down the stairs.

When she arrived at Wilmer & Co., the only person in the shop was Miss Hawke, who was dusting bottles on the counter.

'Hello Miss Carswell,' she said. 'Mr Hocking's in the dispensary. Would you like to go through?'

Katie had not been invited into the dispensary before, and she was surprised by the huge array of bottles and jars on the shelves which covered the walls. A long counter in the centre of the room held several sets of scales. There was a sink and draining board in one corner. The light was dim, as there was only one side window looking out on to a wall, and another which overlooked the back yard.

At first she couldn't see James, but then he came out of the stock room, carrying two large bottles. He didn't see her standing just inside the door, and she didn't say anything until he had put the bottles down on the counter. He seemed preoccupied.

'James?'

He looked up and she caught the sudden warm pleasure in his eyes before he took her in his arms and kissed her.

'Well,' he said at last. 'Good journey?'

'Excellent thank you – and no objections from Pa. I thought he might not want me to come, so late in the season. But if he knew how warm it is down here, compared with home, he'd be very surprised.'

'And your French translating? It Bill back?'

'Yes, but he's off again in the middle of October, so I'll be on duty then, I expect.'

She smiled up at him, straightened the collar of his white coat.

'Shall we go for a walk this evening, or will you be too tired?'

'Of course not. But the nights are drawing in so we can't go too far.'

'I know – though there's nothing wrong with our street lamps. I'm certain they'll ensure our respectability.'

'And we can always go back to Pendennis House. Meg and T.H. won't mind a bit.'

These plans were interrupted by a discreet knock on the door and Miss Hawke entered.

'I'm sorry to interrupt you, Mr. Hocking, but Mr Treleaven's in, wanting your advice about his cough.'

'Right – tell him I'm just coming. Well, Katie, six thirty?'

'I'll be waiting,' she said.

She stayed until James was in deep conversation with Mr Treleaven, then slipped through the shop and out of the door.

They walked along the sea road, slowly, stopping to sit on the seats which the Council had erected for the convenience of the many convalescents who stayed in Falmouth for the sea air.

'By the way', James said, 'Are you busy on Sunday? If not, mother and father would like you to come to tea.'

'Sunday?' Katie was surprised. 'My goodness, I'm quite astonished. No, I'm sure Meg has nothing planned. She would have told me. So please thank them for the invitation, and say I would like to come. But how did this come about?'

James laughed.

'You'd be surprised. I thought I'd ask mother for the first Sunday you were here, and if she refused I knew I'd got a few Sundays in hand to keep asking. Last time, if you remember, I didn't ask her till your holiday was nearly over, so it was easy for her to say no.'

Katie was watching the lights of a large ship as it made its way across the horizon.

'Well, I'll try not to let you down, though I must say I feel a little apprehensive.'

'I'm sure everything will be fine,' said James, though he privately thought nothing of the kind. 'And father will be there of course. He doesn't say very much these days, but I know he looks on you with quite a kindly eye.'

On Sunday, the weather was fine and sunny, and James collected her for a walk after lunch. His mother had stipulated four o'clock as the time for tea, and Katie was anxious that they should not be late. She wore her panama hat with the violet ribbon, her grey skirt, and her favourite blouse that was threaded across the yoke with a similar violet ribbon. The blouse and skirt were neatly drawn together at her slender waist with a grey suede belt. Meg had taken a critical inspection before she left.

'And your grey suede gloves and handbag.' she had remarked. 'Well Katie, you look very well – exactly what a prospective mother-in-law would approve, I should think – though when that lady is Mrs Hocking, who can tell?'

'Thanks Meg,' Katie said, 'That's all the encouragement I need.'

So at two minutes to four precisely, Katie and James turned the corner from Wood Lane into Wodehouse Terrace.

James opened the door and held it for Katie to enter.

'We're here mother,' he called.

There was a pause and then Mrs Hocking appeared beside the stairs, from the back of the hall.

'Good afternoon Miss Carswell,' she said.

Katie remembered only too well not to hold out her hand.

'Good afternoon, Mrs Hocking. It is very kind of you to invite me.'

'James, tell you father that tea is ready, in the dining room. Come along, Miss Carswell.'

Katie followed her to the dining room, where tea was formally laid on the dining table – so, no leisurely informal tea in the sitting room, as they had at home. There was a pause as they listened to James and Mr Hocking approaching very slowly along the passage. Katie had time to take in the green wallpaper which made the light in the room slightly aqueous, the giant fern in a jardinière in front of the window, and a heavy sideboard on which was a long damask runner, an elaborate cut glass cruet and a silver plated egg stand with six plated eggcups and spoons.

Mr Hocking entered, supported on a walking stick, stopped and subjected her to a long gaze.

'Good afternoon, young lady,' he said. 'Uncommonly pretty blouse you're wearing. How do you do?'

He held out his hand and Katie took it quickly.

'Thank you. And how do you do, sir?'

Mrs Hocking interrupted these pleasantries to indicate where Katie should sit, opposite James, and she and Mr Hocking took their accustomed places at each end of the table.

'James, bring in the tea tray, if you please. It's all ready.'

'Yes mother.'

He disappeared and there was a silence. Katie gazed at the beautifully starched white tablecloth, edged with lace, and an array of plates of food – bread and butter, jam – strawberry? Gentleman's Relish, Cornish splits, a dish of clotted cream, cucumber sandwiches and a Victoria sponge cake on an elegant comport taking stage centre.

James brought in the tray with its silver teapot, hot water jug and milk jug. He placed it beside Mrs Hocking.

'Tea, Miss Carswell? Milk? Sugar?'

'Oh, tea and a little milk please. And no sugar.'

Tea poured, bread and butter was handed round. Katie admired the delicacy of the china.

'Do you have afternoon tea at home, Miss Carswell?' Mrs Hocking asked, as if (as Katie thought later) she had sprung from some strange uncivilized tribe in the heathen north.

'Yes indeed we do. We generally have a cup of tea by the fire at four o'clock – usually just my sister Emma and I, and whichever sister or friend has dropped in to see us. Then we have high tea at six o'clock when Pa comes home from the office.'

214

'Really. And your main meal?'

'Och, we usually have dinner at one o'clock, on the dot. Pa comes home you see, and then has a nap before going back to town. This suits him very well, for often in the evenings he goes out again to his club. All his friends meet there, you see, which is good for Pa who gets tired of what he calls "my chattering houseful of girls"'.

Mr Hocking helped himself to Gentleman's Relish.

'How many girls are there then besides you, Miss Carswell?'

'Well, there are nine of us girls, and one boy – most of the girls are married now. My sister Meg is one of the oldest of us.'

'So you are scattered now, if most of them are married?'

'Och yes. But Pa gathers as many of us as he can in the summer and takes us all on holiday to Loch Katrine, to a lovely big house there. He is one of the bailies appointed to the Glasgow Water Board, you see, and most of Glasgow's water comes from Loch Katrine. He mixes business with pleasure in the nicest possible way. We have wonderful holidays there. This year in particular.'

She couldn't resist a glance at James. He was gazing steadily at her, a warning in his eyes.

'And what made this year so particularly enjoyable?' asked Mrs Hocking.

For a second Katie paused. Had the woman seen the glances she and James had exchanged? How easy it was to let her tongue run away with her.

'Well, we all had our special friends there and it was all such fun – and we had a lovely concert one night with singing and Scottish dancing – reels and so on.'

'Would you like to try a split with cream, Katie?' James asked pointedly before she could say any more. 'Try it with some of the strawberry jam.'

'Thank you. I will. What a beautiful colour the jam is, Mrs Hocking. Did you make it?'

'Of course,' said that lady, distantly.

'Mother makes all our preserves, Katie, and the best Cornish pasties in the world.'

Katie was determined not to break the ensuing silence. She knew she had dominated the conversation, as Emma had so often told her, and didn't want to fall into the trap of being considered garrulous and gossipy.

'Tell me, Miss Carswell, what work does your father do?'

She turned to Mr Hocking.

'He's the only manufacturer of medal ribbons in the British Isles.' Katie said proudly. 'He sells to the armed forces here and oh! to many foreign countries.'

'How very interesting,' said Mr Hocking. 'Medal ribbons, eh?'

'Yes, I find it really fascinating. I love to go down to the factory. There are dye vats in one building, and then the weaving sheds. It's a busy place. Then the other part of his business is making fishing flies. They're made by women as he says they have better hands for tying those fiddly little knots and all the tiny feathers and things that make up a fly.'

'More tea, Miss Carswell? A slice of my sponge cake?'

Katie passed her cup and saucer to Mrs Hocking and eyed the sponge cake. It sat high above the table on its comport; the cake itself was impressively tall and was topped with a drift of icing sugar.

'It looks very good,' Katie said, taking a polite sip of her second cup. 'Just a little please.'

James cut the cake. The slice looked enormous on her plate, and Katie, praying that she wouldn't choke on the icing sugar, took a modest bite.

'This is really delicious, Mrs Hocking, and it's so light.'

'Eight eggs in my sponge cakes. The secret of a light result, Miss Carswell, is constant beating. I always beat the mixture for half an hour.'

'Really?' said Katie. 'I'm afraid fifteen minutes is my maximum.'

She felt Mrs Hocking's sharp gaze upon her.

'How many eggs?'

'Usually six.'

Mrs Hocking, lips compressed, fiddled with the tea strainer, pouring more tea for the men.

'And what proportion of sugar and flour?' she asked.

'Well, Cook always taught us that an egg is usually about two ounces, and that we would need an equal weight of flour, butter and sugar for each egg – so six eggs means twelve ounces of flour and so on.'

She was aware now that Mrs Hocking was trying to catch her out.

'I'm surprised that you make cakes, Miss Carswell, if you have a cook. I should have thought the cook is there to do all your cooking.'

Katie glanced at James. He was obviously ill at ease, but remained silent.

'Pa has always made sure that all of us can cook. Our Cook is elderly now, and so Emma and I make all the jam and marmalade, and a sticky time we have of it, I can tell you. But my speciality is chutney. If I'm in a bad mood I can chop up all the enemy apples and onions and things to cheer me up again.'

'Really?' said Mrs Hocking. 'I am surprised. Displays of ill temper are never becoming in a woman.'

Finally James intervened.

'I'm sure Katie's joking mother. Now, if we've finished, perhaps you will show Katie the quilt you're making for the next bazaar.'

They rose. James carried the tea tray back to the kitchen. Katie was about to volunteer to collect the crockery and take that too, when a glance at Mrs Hocking's formidable chin warned her that far from being helpful, she would be judged impolite.

They adjourned to the sitting room, where the quilt was duly admired by Katie, who was truly impressed by the beautiful hand stitching. Then it was time to go.

It was good to be out in the fresh air again, swinging down Wood Lane, hand in hand, the visit over.

'Well done Katie. It wasn't such an ordeal as you imagined, was it?'

Katie smiled.

'There were one or two tricky moments though – mentioning special friends for instance. I hardly dared look at you.'

'You were on thin ice there – and chopping up your victims didn't go down too well, either.'

She began to laugh and together they walked down to the harbour where some of the fishing boats were moored; and leaning on the wall, they gazed at the water beyond where dozens of small craft bobbed at their anchors, rocking gently on the incoming tide.

21

A note:

Tuesday morning

My dearest Kitty,

Will you please give boy Nona's address as I think the weather will be fine today for sending off the cream, and as I have intended sending her some for a long time I want to do so at the earliest opportunity.

He might also bring back T.H.'s camera then I may perhaps get the negatives developed today. I expect Wilmer will be busy rolling and marking the court this morning if the grass is not too sodden.

Goodbye, with love
Jim

The reply on the same piece of paper.

Good morning – am up in good time and done a hard day's washing – not myself – that doesn't take long –

The wee wife's address is 8 Beaton Road, Maxwell Park, Glasgow. She will be very delighted.

Am sending on the camera – don't kill yourself doing these things – with love
Kitty.

Remember T.H.'s ointment – am coming down the village will give you a nod.

The weather held, and they were able to have several games of tennis on Mr Wilmer's carefully rolled court. James was impressed by Katie's aptitude and strength, returning shots from her baseline to his. On two Wednesday afternoons they joined Lilian Head and her partner for hard fought matches.

The nights were drawing in now and Falmouth ladies were beginning to send out invitations for the winter season.

James received an invitation to an evening party from Mr and Mrs Gerard Pascoe who requested the pleasure of the company of Mr J Hocking and friend, on Friday 17th at 7 p.m. – whist and music. An added handwritten note asked him to remember to bring his music.

James immediately sent a note to Pendennis House to ask Katie if she would like to accompany him. The boy brought back the answer speedily.

Dearest Jim,
    Yes, if you would like to go, I will come with you. It's up to you to decide.
    With love, Kitty.

Accordingly on Friday evening, Katie went along with Meg and T.H. who were also invited. Katie was pleased that she had brought an evening dress with her, one that James had not yet seen. It was a pale mint green silk, patterned with white flowers, prettily gathered round the low neck. With it she wore her three strands of pearls and a green comb in her hair, sprinkled with diamante.

When the Sandrys and Katie arrived, there was pleasant social chatter as a number of guests were already there. Mrs Pascoe's drawing and dining rooms, usually divided by folding doors, had been opened up into one large reception room. Chairs were conveniently placed round the walls, and the dining table had been pushed against the wall at one end, its damask cloth covered by dishes containing appetising little sandwiches, vol au vents and tiny cakes. The Pascoes' parties were always well attended.

Katie, having removed her cloak and given it to the maid, entered the room with Meg and T.H. She looked round hastily, but there was no sign of James. He had promised her that he would meet her at the party, as after work he had to go home to change. If he had then gone to meet her at Pendennis House they would have been very late arrivals at the Pascoes.

Mr Pascoe came forward now to greet them, and Meg introduced him to Katie.

'I'm delighted you've been able to come along, Miss Carswell. You're as beautiful as your sister, I see.'

'It was very kind of you to invite me,' Katie said. 'James should be here by now, but I expect he will come along shortly. I can't think what's happened to him.' She glanced at her watch. 'Why, it's nearly nine o'clock.'

She stayed with Meg and T.H. constantly glancing at the door. Meg and T.H. were invited to join another couple at whist in the morning room, but Katie stayed, listening to Mr Pascoe who had claimed her attention again. He chatted amicably to her about tennis.

'Yes, I've been playing down here,' she said. 'The weather in Glasgow is usually too cold and wet by now to play. But here you seem to go on right into November.'

'Well of course it depends on the weather,' he replied. 'We've been lucky this year.'

She glanced again towards the door. Wherever could James be? Beginning to feel really annoyed, she concentrated on what Mr Pascoe had to say.

'And what do you do in the winter months, Miss Carswell,' he was asking. 'I suppose you're tied indoors by the awful Scottish weather.'

'Not a bit of it,' she retorted. 'In the winter we play hockey.'

He raised his eyebrows.

'Really?'

'Yes, really. We have a women's hockey club, generally made up of those of us who were at the same school. We have a hilarious time, get covered in mud, and lose nearly every match we play.'

'I'm so sorry to be late,' said a voice behind her.

'Good to see you James,' said Mr Pascoe, 'Miss Carswell here has just been telling me about these Scottish lassies' daring deeds on the hockey field.'

Katie turned away from James.

'I'm sorry Katie,' he said. 'I really did get held up tonight, of all nights, when I particularly wanted to be early.'

'We usually play at least one match a week,' continued Katie, ignoring James' presence, and sparkling up at Mr Pascoe.

'Even in the snow?' he asked.

She laughed.

'No, no. We couldn't see the lines. The snow can be really heavy in our part of the world.'

'We don't have snow very much down here,' James said.

Katie ignored him.

'We used to go sledging in the park when we were young.' she said.

'Well you're not so very old now.' Mr Pascoe replied gallantly. 'Ah, I see my wife is calling us all to supper.'

'Katie, may I get you some refreshment?' James asked. 'Some lemonade perhaps, and something to eat?'

Katie turned, affecting surprise.

'Oh, there you are James. Yes, I would like some lemonade, if it's not too much trouble.'

She watched James collect two glasses of lemonade which he brought back to her. He looked white, and very angry, and she began to regret her behaviour.

'There are seats over there,' he said, indicating a quiet corner of the room. He led the way towards two chairs, half hidden by Mrs Pascoe's large pot ferns.

They sat down and he gave her the lemonade. There was silence for a few moments, but Katie knew that a storm was brewing.

'Whatever came over you Katie, to be so very rude to me in public?' James hissed.

'You were the rude one,' Katie retorted in defence. 'Turning up an hour-and-a- half late. I hardly knew what to say to people. And there were so many that I didn't know, and you should have been there introducing me to them. I couldn't stand there all night talking to Meg and T.H. and Mr Pascoe. He introduced himself, by the way, and had the courtesy to talk to me. Goodness knows what he was thinking.'

James shifted in his chair.

'I've already apologised for being late. Mr Wilmer was unwell and I took over his evening duty so he could go home and rest.'

'You could have let me know,' Katie said.

'Tonight that was impossible. The shop was full of people waiting for their prescriptions. Harry goes off at six. He stayed till seven tonight. Miss Hawke stayed on till eight, then she had to go. She has an invalid mother. I can't just turn away sick people.'

'Well when you take over, you'll have to decide how better to organise things. People should be told that the shop closes at a certain time, and you must stick to it.'

'Has it occurred to you Katie, that these people are our customers? They come into the shop and are under our care. It's not like selling loaves of bread or a leg of lamb. When Mr Wilmer retires, they will by <u>my</u> customers, and if I don't satisfy their needs, I will soon have no business at all.'

'I still think times could be re-arranged. After all, you've got to have some time off. Why, Pa always finishes on the dot, and he'll arrange to finish early if he has some engagement to go to.'

'You forget, Katie. Your father has most of his working life behind him. Now, at this time of life, he can afford to take things a little easier. I can't.'

They were silent for a few moments as another couple came to sit quite close to them.

Katie turned to him.

'I suppose you're right. But it <u>was</u> horrid waiting all that time for you. Everybody was looking at me.'

'I expect they were admiring that very pretty dress you're wearing.'

'I doubt it.'

He turned away from her, glowering at the chattering guests. Suddenly she was afraid.

'Oh Jim, please say I'm forgiven. Please – be nice.'

He remained obdurate for a few moments, and then, to her relief, he turned to her, took her hand and smiled wryly.

'Of course you're forgiven. But never do that to me again.'

'No, I won't. I promise.'

For a while they sat in silence thankful that the quarrel was over, aware only of each other, oblivious of the fact that the musical part of the evening was starting. But the first notes from Miss Ida Beard, a somewhat strident soprano, brought them back to the present.

'I can't sing tonight,' James whispered. 'When Ida's finished, let's leave.'

'Yes, do let's.'

Accordingly they apologised to their hostess, who expressed surprise that this healthy young woman should be smitten with a terrible headache.

Soon they were out in the cool air, refreshing after the heat of the crowded room, and set off for Pendennis House.

'Do we have to go straight home?' Katie asked. 'Couldn't we have a wee look at the sea? If Meg gets home before us, she's sure to leave the door on the latch.'

They reached the road above the cliffs and could hear the waves running up the beach. The road was deserted, the lights of the Falmouth Hotel behind them and the starlit sky their only guide.

Although together now, their harsh words had shaken them and they sought to forget their argument in the warmth and tenderness of their growing love.

22

The twelfth of October brought a letter from Nona, addressed to Wodehouse Terrace:

8 Beaton Road
Maxwell Park
11th Oct

Dear Mr Jimmy,

Many thanks for the cream that has just arrived. It was ever so good of you to remember to send it. I am looking forward to have a really Cornish tea tonight.

When are you going to send my dear sister home again? We miss her in this little corner of the globe and her parent missed her last night when he was dressing in his uniform to go to a dinner party. Katie dressed him last time, and last night when I arrived he was struggling before the mirror with the gardener jumping round him. It was intensely comic but nobody saw the joke but myself. However he got off in time with his sword on at his left side, not hanging down his back as Katie fixed it.

Emma has been away too but comes back today. I do miss dropping in for a free meal when I'm hungry and my own cupboard is bare. Hubby sends his love and hopes to see you at Christmas, when our spare room will be at your disposal.

Thanking you again for the cream.

Yours very sincerely
F. Nona McCall.

They leaned on a field gate, the hills rolling away to the west. The meadows were dusty green in the sunlight and further away grew a purple haze of heather. Bracken was turning too, rust on the rough ground and a blackberry briar curved high above them, its berries ripening belatedly from pink to purple.

'It would be lovely if you <u>could</u> come up for Christmas.' Katie said. 'If only for a few days – I know you can't stay till Hogmanay, but as you're closed Christmas Day and Boxing Day, you could come up on Christmas Eve and go home a day or two after Boxing Day. Oh, I do wish you would – it would make Christmas really special.'

James thought of previous Christmas Eves in the shop; they usually stayed open on that night for as long as customers came in. Often this was to buy a last minute present of soap or perfume, or to stock up on cough mixtures and indigestion cures. Sometimes a doctor's prescription would be brought in, and although officially they were closed for the following days, either he or Mr Wilmer had to be ready to open the shop for an urgent prescription.

'I'd love to come Katie. But Christmas is <u>really</u> busy, and comes at the end of a frantic week. I daren't even go to sleep after Christmas Dinner, in case I'm called out to dispense something or other.'

'That's really disappointing,' Katie sighed. 'But if you find you can come at the last minute, please do. I know Nona is looking forward to putting you up – you'll be her first overnight visitor and they love to entertain. Anyway, it would be the ideal opportunity to ask Pa.'

'Yes, it would be easier than writing to him. You can't gauge people's reactions when they receive your letter – face to face is much better. And I don't think we should declare our engagement until after I've got your Pa's approval.'

Katie was obviously disappointed.

'Well, if you don't meet him at Christmas, goodness knows when you'll meet. Next summer seems an awfully long time away. Couldn't you write whilst I am down here? Go on Jimmy, then we'll be engaged and I can start making things to go into my hopeful box.'

But James would not be persuaded. When he felt the right time had come, he would write. At present his mind was busy with many things – the impending purchase of the shop for one, and it had occurred to him that being the owner of a pharmacy, rather than just a junior assistant, would make a much better impression on a successful business man, as he knew Mr Carswell to be, when he wrote the proposal letter. He couldn't forget the incident at the Pascoe's party, either, when Katie's behaviour must have been noticeable to a good many of the thirty or so people who had attended. He had been quick to notice the sympathetic and ironic glances he had received across the counter in the days that followed.

At last he had a sudden inspiration as to the next step. He would buy her a piece of jewellery that would be beautiful but which would not have the connotations of an engagement ring, but that she would be able to wear as a preliminary to the official betrothal.

Whilst he had been training in London he had visited Faudel's the Jewellers to buy a brooch for his mother's birthday. He remembered this now, and wrote to them immediately. He imagined a gold bracelet might be suitable, but one of the town jewellers might show curiosity as to whom the recipient might be. Much better to have the anonymity of the London firm.

Two days later a parcel arrived, at the shop!

Faudels 36/40 Newgate Street
London EC
Gold Jewellery Department

18.10.06

On approbation for 3 days. The goods remain the
property of Faudels until invoiced.

857H 1 x 9ct Gold Curb Chain Bracelet	*2. 5.0.*
695H 1 x 9ct " " " "	*2.17.6*
651 1 x Solid " " " "	*2.10.0*
83 1 x " " " " "	*3. 7.6*
613H 1 x 15ct Gold curb bracelet	*3. 5.0*
156C 1 x 15ct " " "	*4. 7.6*

Signed Reg D
4

He was alone in the dispensary that morning, and pulled off the string. Each bracelet was packed in a gold 'Faudel's' box. He took them out and laid them on the counter. At a glance they all looked very similar. He checked each one against the list. Finally he decided on the one marked 613H and asterisked it in the margin of the list.

He repacked the others, enclosed a cheque for three pounds five shillings (phew!) and instructed the post office assistant to send it off by registered post.

He was due to go to the Sandrys' for supper, much to his mother's displeasure, and after closing went straight to Pendennis House. Katie answered the door.

'Come into the morning room,' she said, 'Meg thought we would be more comfortable here.'

A bright fire was burning and the room was warm and well lit.

'Meg and T.H. are going out this evening and coming back with their friends for a late supper. Ours is already on the table. Come and sit down. I'll just go and get the coffee pot.'

James sat at the table, checking in his pocket that the little blue box with the bracelet was safely there. The table was laid with a simple supper of cold ham, beetroot in a glass dish, celery, rolls, butter and a fruit cake.

Katie returned with the coffee and poured it out.

'It's almost as if we are married,' she said.

'Breakfast together in Scotland, now supper in Falmouth.'

Katie in Falmouth, Autumn 1906
Photo taken by James

After they had eaten, they took their coffee to drink before the fire, sitting on the settee which faced it – James talking about several incidents in the shop that day, and Katie recounting her walk around the town.

'Look what I bought today. Wasn't it naughty?' She produced a box of chocolates.

Later, when he felt the right moment had arrived, James took out the blue box.

'Katie,' he said, interrupting her in the middle of some inconsequential talk.

'Yes?'

He was suddenly uncertain. What if she didn't like the bracelet? Should he have allowed her to choose for herself? However, it was too late now.

'Katie, I should like to give you this as a promise of my love.'

He saw her glance at the box, saw the flush rise in her throat to suffuse her cheeks.

'Oh Jim -'

He took the bracelet from the box and clasped it round her left wrist. He looked up and couldn't mistake the pang of disappointment that crossed her face. Damn, he should have bought the ring and to hell with her father and his mother and everyone else.

'It's … it's beautiful Jim. Thank you so very much.'

They kissed. Her face was clear again and she turned her wrist in the firelight to see the gold links flicker and glisten.

'It's lovely Jim. I'll wear it every day, though you won't forget my engagement ring, will you?'

'I won't. I promise – just as soon as I have your father's permission.'

This first evening in the little room, being comfortable before the fire, able to have time and space

231

to talk, uninhibited by interruptions, drew them closer together.

In their different ways, they were to remember these evenings for ever.

Katie showing her gold bracelet. Autumn 1906
Photo taken by James

23

Telegram:
Handed in at *Central Cal Glasgow* at *6.25 p.m.*
Received at *Falmouth 6.51 p.m. 23.10.06*

To: James Hocking. 8 Market Strand, Falmouth.

Arrived thriving. K.O.C.

Murcia
Tuesday Evening 23rd

My dearest Jim

You ought to be coming in now as I write this, it's just your hour but no such luck – you'd get my wire so know I arrived safely.

I didn't sleep much – had a bit of a headache and thus wiled away the hours thinking of you in your new coat as I left you, looking so sweet. I got the carriage to myself the whole way and was glad – don't like to be caught in my weak moments, except you, you don't count!

I got a handsome [sic] *and drove to Euston and had a very enjoyable breakfast indeed after a good wash.*

I ate your grapes about five in the morning, got as dry as a wooden god and instead of taking two as you advised I ate the whole bunch right off, and they were splendid. I told Em you'd said I might eat two, that wouldn't do me any harm, so she laughed and told me I must do without coddling as she hadn't time.

233

Harry, Winkie and Nona came in and joined us at tea – and then they all went off to a concert and I stayed at home and got my things unpacked so am now waiting to have a good chat with Miss E when she comes in.

I hope you are missing me and not enjoying life for a bit. I am missing you awfully. I am glad to get the journey over; it is long and I did feel so dumpy. You would get home pretty late, did you not?

Now dear good-night and excuse epistle – am tired and needing some beauty sleep and it's getting late. With heaps of love-

Yours, Kitty.

James had got home late. He had accompanied Katie to Truro to catch the night train to London, seeing her safely onto the train and putting her luggage in the charge of the guard, whom he tipped, giving him the task of making sure that the young lady was safe and comfortable and reunited with her luggage at Paddington. He then caught the last train back to Falmouth, arriving near midnight.

Next morning, he rose early and was at the shop before seven thirty, to write to Katie in the quiet of the attic room. How he had hated leaving her, so small and vulnerable, on that overnight train. She should be in London now, taking a cab from Paddington to Euston – at least the second part of her long journey would be accomplished in daylight. He poured all his longing and concern for her into the letter, ran downstairs and along to the main post office to catch the earliest post out.

Murcia.
Friday Morning.

My dearest Jim,

As I can't have Tea with you as I did a week ago I am coming to supper to see you hide away the beefsteak, so see and mind your manners.

It's ages since Tuesday and yet its only Friday and I am missing you terribly dear.

I was sorry you'd only got my letter on Thursday morning. I was too late in getting home to post one before seven so of course it didn't go that night. I got yours with my coffee on Wednesday morning, and it was sweet and I am so glad you are going to miss me even though I did load you with wet parcels at dinner time.

I have been so busy since I came back getting some clothes, it's very cold here, quite winter – though nice and bright. Everybody here thinks I am thinner so your machine must be wrong, though I fancied I was getting fat myself, I must say.

Nona enjoyed the cream so much – said she determined to eat it and made herself quite ill overeating in case it'd turn sour, took too much in case any might be wasted.

I've got some news which will amuse you, I think. Pa got home the night after I did and I saw that he was pretty suspicious so I just told him and he was quite nice about it. I think he was better pleased than being left in the dark any longer. On the whole I am quite relieved as I used to worry in case he'd get hold of your letters. Now it doesn't matter in the least. He said to Em that you looked a nice fellow, so he evidently noticed you at Loch Katrine right enough, thus you need not worry about coming here in the Spring. You won't be eaten up so you must be sure and come.

I wonder what you're doing just now, it's not your dinner time yet – possibly making eyes at the window and gossiping about the size of Miss So-and-so's waist and whether she suffers much in consequence thereof.

Winkie was asking for you and I told her there was someone looked out to suit her, but she hankers after the moon and an ordinary star seems mundane and undesirable.

The appointment Winkie hoped for is all up. Another doctor is elected, so that's another disappointment but she is looking so well and very bright. She throws off her troubles so well, but it is jolly hard lines.

Have you flitted your (or rather my) leggings from Pendennis yet? Not to mention the wee pipe which was such a companion to me when I was housekeeper?

I didn't quite believe that you woke up every quarter of an hour on Monday night but I take the will for the deed. By the way, I hope the toothache is quite gone and that peace now reigns at Wodehouse.

I told Harry I was not to play hockey any more, but she only laughed and said I was their only hope in time of need, so as a duty I must, I suppose.

Now my dear, good night – write soon – and sometimes think of

Yours lovingly, Kitty.

24

Letters flew back and forth during November, Katie writing as promised on Tuesdays and Fridays and James responded on Wednesdays and Sundays. He had developed all the Loch Katrine group photographs and they were very successful, everybody looking in the right direction at the right moment.

Murcia
Friday

My dearest Jim,
    Thanks immensely for the photos – they are splendid, all three are fine, and the group is very distinct, though I do look like a sick pig.
    Fancy you having your half day on Wednesday when I was out west playing that match – it was fine, good field and we only lost three goals so that was an improvement compared with fourteen at the previous one, was it not? Am so stiff I can scarcely move from one room to t'other, but I wasn't so soft as I expected after two months of laziness. Harry took cramp and I had to carry her off the pitch at the end and stuff her with tea and she was soon all right ...
    It's a beastly, wet, dark, miserable, creepy day so I intend crawling up to call for Clara as its her (at home) day, and it's only next door. I have now got a few clothes so can venture forth with my usual air of dignity.
    Poor Tommy Reid, who was never so well as he was with us, is dying and suffers great pain – so

*everyone hopes the end of the week will see him
with his troubles ended. Poor man – he was a nice
old soul in spite of drawbacks. Father is losing so
many friends, it makes a great difference to him as
he is too old to make new ones now.*

*Glad your cold is better and I am sure your
beauty is restored again...*

*On Wednesday night we had Hallow e'en, a
Scotch custom, when you burn and eat nuts, so
Harry came in with us after the match and we had
great fun. We burned Harry first with another,
and if one of the nuts jumps away of course it
means it's not the right man, and the two nuts were
scarcely in when one jumped clean away into
another part of the fire altogether. Next we put in
Winkie and the nuts went clean out almost at once
so she was quite upset, and then I put in you and I,
and we burned up as nicely as anything and died
out naturally so I was crowing over the others –
and Em was very lucky. She put in two lots and
they burned equally, so she is evidently easily
suited.*

*Now I think I've written enough rubbish. See
and take a good supper, though it's bad for you at
such an unearthly hour. You are not nearly well
enough looked after. Goodbye dear,*

Yours lovingly, Kitty.

Writing to James that the burning of the chestnuts was
"great fun", Katie was secretly very pleased that hers had
"burned up nicely as anything", for ever since he had
given her the beautiful gold bracelet there had been a
small nagging doubt at the back of her mind. Although
she had accepted his reasoning that they couldn't

become publicly engaged until he had written to or preferably met her father, she had hoped, nevertheless, that when she returned home she would be proudly wearing his engagement ring.

As it was, she had to face Em, Nona, Winkie and Harry with what she realised was a reason that sounded hollow even to her, as she told them.

"Well?" Emma had asked when she had gone into the drawing room on her return home.

The others had crowded round and there was an abundance of hugs and kisses before they dropped back.

'Come on,' Em had continued, 'Show us the ring.'

She had held out her hand.

'No ring', she had said bravely, 'But a lovely bracelet.'

They surrounded her again, admiring the gift, but she was sure there was a growing doubt in their eyes.

'James needs to see Pa before we become officially engaged. He wants to follow the correct procedure.'

'Quite right,' said Winkie.

'Will he be coming up for Christmas?' Nona asked. 'Our spare room's all ready for him. We've redecorated it and it's looking really smart.'

'No, not Christmas. They're always frantically busy then, what with presents and cures for indigestion and flu and coughs. But he's planning a break at Easter. But even that is a bit doubtful, because it depends on when he takes over the business.'

'But a letter to Pa would solve the whole thing,' Em said. 'Then you could get engaged and be married in the summer.'

'A summer wedding, how lovely,' Winkie said. 'Rose petal confetti and the sun shining on the bride,' said Nona, already dreamily imagining the scene, Katie thought by the faraway look in her eyes.

Harry remained silent, but Katie thought she saw doubt and concern in her expression.

'Well, what have you been up to?' Em asked, 'though perhaps I need hardly ask. Six weeks you've been away, do you realise?'

'I know, a long time,' Katie replied, 'but well worth it. Falmouth is so warm and friendly, and the sea is practically on Meg's doorstep.'

Tea arrived, carried in by Bessie, and several cups were drunk before the rest of the party went off to a concert in town. They pressed Katie to come too, but she was tired and wanted to unpack her belongings. She also hoped to write to Jim, following up the wire, to assure him she'd arrived safely.

Another, post marked November 9th:

Murcia
Friday evening.

My dearest Jim,

Sorry to read that you have another cold. I think there must be something up as you have had too many. Don't go into the window so often – you can get quite a fair view of the waists in the town without catching so many nasty colds.

Thanks, I had a very good birthday though no self respecting girl has them after twenty five – they come of course but there's no need for a public demonstration about the fact, however I really enjoyed it very much in spite of their number.

We are getting it very cold and wintry. Em and I have just walked out from town, it was lovely and crisp, and I am now waiting on the Baillie (Pa) for tea. He's very late and we can't imagine what's up as he's usually in good time.

We are all going to a big bazaar tomorrow. The girl students are getting it up – it's to make their place as nice as the men's, and the Princess Royal opens it, so it's the place to be at this week of course whether you buy or not. They wish £10,000 and have already got six so they hope to have it by Saturday. You can see it's a little bigger than the Wesley one. There is a lovely motor to be raffled so Nona, Em, Harry, Winkie and I have bought a ticket, each giving a shilling so if we get it and sell it for £500 we will each get £100. So we hope to have the lucky number. Do you think there's any hope for us? It's given heaps of fun anyway and we don't expect to win it of course.

Bill is still away so I get some ghastly epistles to write; one man from Paris sent a very impudent note asking for some small order of things, saying he would pay sometime but not soon – so I got an answer to send him, asking him if he knew he was writing to the only manufacturer of the thing in the kingdom and unless he paid, he'd have to wait for them. Em and I had great fun out of it – hope to goodness it was put down right, it's so funny to read all their different complaints. Some of them speak very plainly at times. However, it seems to make enough to keep two old maids in very decent comfort so we have a good time ...

Now my dear, I must be coiling up or you will be bored perusing this epistle. Good night deary, sleep off your cold and take a good morning in bed.

Yours lovingly Kittie.

241

P.S. Pa is just in and has been at the council all this time and all the convenors have been changed so he is no longer "convenor of the waterworks". To change every three years was finally voted for today, and was won by a vote, so he has just one more year at that lovely spot as he will retire from the council next November having lost his only interest. He takes it very well and is quite good natured over it, of course, everyone being in the same box is a comfort.

We are sorry as it took up his time and gave him an interest – everything has an end this side Jordan. Now you can really get to sleep. I won't keep you any longer – seemed to have a lot to say tonight. K.O.C.

James must have spent all spare letter writing time corresponding with Katie, for on the 14th he had a short note from brother Edward. He was very busy in the shop, and there were changes at home too. He and Edward had conferred about Mrs Hocking's health. Ever since her chesty cough and cold in the summer, she had lacked energy and was very tired. The doctor suggested that she should have more help in the house. With their parents' consent, they had advertised for a lady help, who would do most of the cooking and some light cleaning, and a new maid, now that the former one had left to get married. In time, they appointed a Miss Barley for the first position, and a young maid, a girl who had just left school, to be trained by Mrs Hocking and Miss Barley.

Dunstable
13.11.06

Dear James,

I should be glad of a letter from you telling me a little about Katie's visit and what sort of time you had while she was there. I haven't had a letter from you ever since I have been back from my holidays.

Mother seems to speak pretty well of Miss Barley and the new maid. What do you think of the change? Any improvement or otherwise?

When do you think of taking over the business at the Strand? Anything settled yet? I don't suppose there is or I should have heard I daresay. Hope it won't be long before you do.

Your loving Bro
Edward
Hope your cold is better.

Murcia
13th November 1906

My dearest Jim,
We haven't heard who's got the motor, it's to be published today … they got £9,000 at the bazaar – very good I think considering the number of bazaars on here just now. We enjoyed it very much on Saturday. I got such a dear wee carved stool, a bargain of course, for my "hopeful box", but the entertainments were very poor. We were just in a fit with them – they were awful.

243

Pa has quite got used to his loss of the convenorship and of course it's right enough that the term should be limited to three years, as some men quite unfit get in and that's a good way of disposing of them but we will miss the visit there every summer very much. Of course you can always revisit the old haunts but it's not quite the same, so this will be our last trip to Invergyle – how things change in this vale of tears. As if I'd ever leave the burning sun of bonnie Scotland to motor to the Cornish Riviera where everyone knows that it rains every day except my eight weeks this time.

I've got the table right in on the fire so am feeling quite snug but its fine and frosty and crisp outside. We are playing a match today against awful savages, so Em is away getting the tea ordered and I ought to be tidying up the wee shanty we use to dress in, but instead am benefiting you by writing.

I am glad to hear mother is simmering down and at least not giving you the benefit of my misdeeds. I suppose she will get your supper again now, although I believe it's about as bad for you to get it as not.

I am glad the day is getting nearer when you will give Glasgow the treat of beholding you in your new coat. It's three weeks today since I left London – it seems much longer. I wish it were just three weeks to seeing you again.

Am off to don my nailed boots and then battle to do or die.

Yours lovingly
Kitty.

James enjoyed her long newsy letters which were a mirror of the way she chatted – lively and often inconsequential and usually amusing.

During November Meg invited him to tea one Wednesday afternoon when he was not on duty. To James Meg was the older and mellower version of Katie; he admired her aura of calm and her practicality. She was cheerful too, obviously happy as T.H.'s wife and with her housekeeping, which was meticulous.

Over tea she spoke affectionately of Katie, asked him directly if he was intending that they should be engaged. What did his mother think of this? He assured her that his mother appeared to be more accepting of Katie, though he thought her attitude would always be strained. Meg promised him that she would help Katie settle in Falmouth if and when they were married.

Murcia
Friday

My dearest Jim

I hope Meg entertained you well on Wednesday, however, I need not trouble to say anything as I know you think she is perfection, and never will allow me to have my say. She wrote me some time ago and said she'd met you, not another word but that. She never says anything in her epistles the least interesting by any chance. Most folk would have said what you had been talking about and if you looked nice etc.; however perhaps you didn't and she wasn't going to lie about it merely to fill a letter up...

Imagine dear, the motor has gone to America, to a man in Long Island, so we haven't got it, however we are glad the neighbours haven't – it would have irritated us to have seen it running about here every day and not us inside it. Scotch people have such Christian spirit one towards t'other, is it beautiful to see...

You will be very relieved dear if that shop does get let to some people who won't interfere with your pale pills for pink people. I think friend Wilmer was correct and the place is not just in the first modern style, but your changes will soon make it very peachy. You have merely to put yourself in the window and the place would be filled at once. Isn't that so?

Bill is coming home tomorrow so 8 Beaton Road is in great commotion. Nona is quite inflated because he wrote and informed her there was no one half as nice in Paris.

It would be very good for you to get a nice dog as you have far too little exercise and are too much taken up with pills by a long way, it's like pulling a tooth to get you to take your holidays.

Do you remember the curate at Loch Katrine? He has been in Glasgow often and has been proposing to Em every visit of course. Em says, 'I'm not cut out for the ministry.' Imagine Em with mother's meetings and all the other drawbacks the clergy are heir to. I am afraid he will need to try his luck elsewhere.

Yours lovingly,
Kitty.

James found Katie's references to Meg very irritating. It lowered Katie in his esteem. After all, Meg and T.H. had been very kind to them, especially on Katie's last stay, when their little morning room had been given over to them in the evenings, with a bright fire, and delicious suppers, perhaps ham sandwiches, or soup for Katie to reheat, cake or fruit jellies. He had noticed that his indigestion had all but gone in those weeks.

He was surprised to receive a card from Stanley.

Penlee, Newbury
Nov. 18. 06

Dear Jimmy,

If you have not fixed up with that Falmouth biz, don't do so yet, as H.R.M. may not go in after all – I will try and let you know more in the course of a week or so.

Yrs affy
Stan.

Too late: the purchase of Wilmer's was now going well, though he was concerned that the shop for sale along the road might go to one of the new multiple chemists, possibly Timothy White and Taylor. He wrote immediately to Stanley to say that he had now settled for Falmouth.

Murcia
Monday Evening

My dearest Jim,

I perused your epistle at the fire just before tea and was greatly benefited thereby. I thought it wasn't coming, as the post was very late ...

Don't get fat whatever you do dear, as I am not going to put on your boots for you, it's so unromantic and savours too much of T.H.

I am so busy this week as I am collecting again, how quickly the time comes round – and the wee dogs are still as barking as ever, but they must be faced, and we've a match tomorrow so I am writing you in the quiet of the evening in spite of Nona and Em having a gossip at the fire, and Bill is in having a business chat with Pa. He is glad to get back after all his travelling...

I don't think you were altogether pleased at me saying it was like drawing a tooth etc, but dear, I do appreciate your steadiness in spite of the above observation, as I know it means a great deal and I would not have you different, unless when I am in a nasty temper which of course is as rare as flowers in June ...

Don't eat too much and upset yourself. I don't at all approve of your feeding hours but I am too far away to interfere, I'm afraid. Em and I go to a luncheon party on Wednesday. I much prefer that to a dance – expect I must be getting old. Bill was asking for you.

Goodbye dear,
Kitty.

James had at last got round to developing and printing the photographs he had taken at Loch Katrine, and sent copies to several of the people in the group.

Murcia
Friday

My dearest Jim,

Em was charmed with the photo but is too lazy to write and say so, and she says I am not to say that – she knows it's so near the truth, but what's the use of me telling crams for her? She is at the window at present and says she is going to write so you may get it some time.

What a crusty bad temper you were in when you wrote last, goodness! Everybody was getting it dished up hot. I was just waiting for my turn to come.

Can't you take a Tourist's ticket to Newbury and go via Glasgow. Surely it's quite on the way perhaps a little longer. You are quite right dear not to give Wilmer all he wants, he is naturally biased in his own favour and is not suited to give an opinion. Would you have any time in London or just one day to do everything? You will be thankful when it's all settled up and finished for good, then you can put on your little boots and pack your bag for the north, as you will need a change of air before beginning seriously. It's such a mistake not to take every care of your health. Of course I am thinking of that alone – as you will quite understand. Nothing selfish ever finds a resting place in K.O.???

Pa went away last night so Winkie, Harry, Em and I, after a nice cosy tea here went in to see "The Prodigal Son". It was so tragic we were all in tears, and just got in after eleven. It was a splendid night and Bessie had a nice little supper ready.

The little ankles are still there in spite of the dogs. I'll get the loan of your leggings another time.

Now dear, goodbye,
Yours lovingly Kitty

From Emma.

POSTCARD   Nov 26. 06   POST MARK TO MARKET STRAND.

Dear Jim

How can I thank you for the sweet photo you sent me. I do appreciate the thought of such a busy man as you.

Hoping this finds you well.
Yours truly
Emma C.

FROM NONA.

8 Beaton Road
Maxwell Park

25th Nov.

Dear James,

As hubby has been so busy since coming home from Spain he has asked me to write and thank you for the most interesting photo you so kindly sent.

I think it is a splendid group and does the photographer great credit. As usual Miss K.O. stands out with her habitual 'only woman on earth' sort of look.

Bill was away in Paris a whole three weeks so I was a most miserable grass widow and didn't enjoy it at all.

I hope you are keeping well and going strong, also Edward, me brudder. Are we to see you up North soon and welcome you on top of the Christmas tree? I hope so.

We were glad to get our famous half back again in our hockey team. I haven't lost quite so many goals since though I'm ashamed to confess nor have we gained any. Famous club we shall be if we get through the whole year without one little goal!

The weather has turned wonderfully mild for this time of year – really quite delightful and yet folks grumble that it is unseasonable and so forth.

Are you interested in Rugby? Wasn't it grand Scotland beating the South Africans? The excitement was intense in Glasgow that day and I guess all the youths about town have had headaches next day.

Kindest regards from Hubby and self and many thanks for the photo.

Yours very sincerely,
F. Nona McCall.

25

Mrs Hocking had had a busy time introducing Miss Barley and the new maid, Connie, to the work required of them. Already though, it was a great relief not to have the responsibility of luncheon ready on the dot of one – that was Miss Barley's duty now; and afterwards she was enjoying the little nap she was taking on her bed, stays loosened, the curtains half closed and the everyday sounds of the town a pleasant murmur in the distance.

Today was bright and sunny, a mild November morning, and she remembered that she hadn't yet sorted out the men's summer suits and coats, for professional cleaning, or for spot cleaning at home.

She went briskly into James' bedroom and opened the wardrobe door. Just as she thought, his good summer suit was hanging there beside his light coat. Taking out the suit, she laid it on the bed and immediately became aware of a strong scent. What was it? Oh yes – lilies of the valley. She picked up the jacket. By sniffing various parts of it, she traced the scent to one arm. She knew that it would be difficult to remove the smell; tweeds retained smells and it was notoriously difficult to remove them. James would have to take it to the cleaners and warn them about the sleeve.

She checked the pockets to make sure they were empty. To her surprise there was a flat hard shape in the right hand pocket. How strange that he had left his business card case here. He usually kept it in the breast pocket of his work suit.

She pulled it out. It was not his card case. It was a small rectangular book with a green embossed cover. She turned it over. There was gold lettering, "Callander and the Trossachs". Whatever was his interest in this? She dropped the jacket onto the bed so that she could inspect the book properly. Opening it, she found it was a series of folded photographs, starting with "Callander Bridge and Ben Ledi." She stretched it across the bed – ten photographs – "The Silver Strand – Loch Katrine, "Ellen's Isle – Loch Katrine" – pictures of a calm loch and wooded islands, a mountain, high in the background. Inside the back cover was a printed label:

M. McARTHUR
Bookseller and Fancy Stationer
Guide Books, Photographs, Artists' Colours
White-wood goods with Local Views.
(opposite the Post Office)
CALLANDER

The little book was new, yet a few dried crumbly fragments dropped from it onto the bedspread. She felt in the pocket again, and sure enough, her fingers met a twig of some plant. She drew it out. It was a sprig of dry white heather.

As she stared at it, a dreadful suspicion became lodged in her mind. Photographs, lily of the valley, heather, SCOTLAND. James had been to Scotland, doubtless to see that scheming little good-for-nothing. But when?

Then she remembered how late in the week of his holiday his second letter had come, surprisingly short of news of the Gravesend relations. He always wrote immediately on his arrival to assure them of his safe journey, which she had received the next day, but the second …

She pondered the time scale. He must have been up to Scotland and then sent his letter when he returned to

Gravesend. But that couldn't be right, for it would mean that he stayed in Scotland only for a night or so. She considered this, and then a blinding realisation struck her. Of course, the whole family at Gravesend were all in the plot. That was it. And probably Edward too.

Waves of rage threatened to overcome her. She sank onto the bed, crumpling the photographs.

The humiliation. All the Gravesend relations, the Clarkes too, no doubt, must all have been in this dreadful conspiracy. All laughing at her, behind her back.

How could he have done this to her? And why? She couldn't have stopped him going to Scotland, if only he'd told her. It was all the fault of that young hussy Katie. It was she who had induced him to scheme and lie to his mother. Neither of her sons had held back anything from her before, of that she was sure. Until now. Now she could no longer be certain.

Eventually she rose and threw the remains of the heather into the waste paper basket. She refolded the photographs into the book covers and slipped it into the pocket of her starched morning apron. Yes. She would take time to decide what action to take. She had the upper hand. He must think he had got away with it. Should she tell her husband, or should she bide her time awaiting the right opportunity?

She replaced the suit in the wardrobe, beginning to plan her campaign as she walked slowly down the stairs.

26

James was having second thoughts about buying the business. Perhaps it would have been better to have waited to see what Stanley Hickman and his father could have offered. After work on Saturday, he had stayed behind at the shop, as he usually did these days, to cash up and balance the books. Takings were far below the summer figures. If they persisted, he would not be able to support a wife and house on the income, and repaying the bank loan would be included in the regular expenses of course.

Writing to Katie the next day, his parents having gone to chapel, he mentioned his despondency to her, in case their plans had to be delayed for a year or two. He also gave her the news that Miss Barley, who had only been with them for a couple of months or so, had given notice as she had become engaged to a wealthy, elderly admirer. This news had thrown the senior Hockings into great turmoil, and already he had advertised for a replacement.

From Katie. Postmarked 27.11.06.

Murcia.
Tuesday

My dearest Jim,
You were in the blues on Saturday were you? Just because you didn't have a nice tea opposite to cheer you into spirits, not that you said so but I am saying it for you.

You can't expect to make so much in the dead of winter when everything is dripping wet and folk have their rents to pay, and it will be far more interesting for you when it is your own.

Em and Nell don't go up to London now till after Xmas.

It was so like your impudence to imagine that I'd require to be told who to vote for – much more likely I'd have to see you voted for the right man, however, of course it's merely householders and I won't be that unless I am an old maid so you wouldn't need to bother.

We had such a nice weekend with second cousin Vi, she is such a charming girl, so musical, plays every instrument under the sun, comes to Glasgow for lessons on the harp, so she'll be all right some day. A neighbour, now dead and the daisies sprouting overhead, once said she was a good looking edition of me, and we are rather alike. Her sister married Professor Kennedy of Edinburgh and she is a great woman's righter, speaks beautifully all over the country. So Vi was telling Pa of her and he says the platform woman is an abomination, and when we said for argument! Why shouldn't there be a female prime minister? He fled to his papers in disgust. His ideas are very antiquated of course, thinks women should merely darn socks all day and agree with man in all his absurdities.

I was over at Dennis town at McCall's. The two kids were having a whist drive. that's Bill's young brothers. Nona got the prize and Tom, Aggie's man, the other, so the in-laws did well, the visitors didn't have a look in. Such a dripping night and I forgot slippers, so had to get a pair of

257

Mother McCalls which were comic to say the least of it but they did all right. It took me so long to get the mud off. Had just finished a hockey match, was too hurried to remember everything. You wouldn't have owned me dear had you seen me come in but you might had you seen me go out again cleaned up. I laughed at myself in the glass for ages. I was a sight for the gods and no mistake.

Did I tell you Winkie is to be the fortune teller at our bazaar next week in a wee tent, got up in a gypsy costume – won't she be comic? She's so good at it and will make a few pounds in a good cause.

Miss Barley seems to be going to have a very good time. She doesn't look exactly suited to a carriage and pair, but that invariably happens in this badly arranged world. Think how elegant I'd look in a nice one. But pills can't manage such things so "Shank's bus" will need to do instead. You are pretty severe on the man, but you see he can afford to have a few faults under those circumstances.

I don't know how it is dear that you come to such a drizzling country for your annual outing – be sure and not make the same mistake again – if you're not careful you may, you know.

Goodbye dear
Yours lovingly
Kitty.

I upset my scent bottle on your letter, it fell onto it when I was dressing.

From Katie. Postmarked 30.11.06.

Murcia
Friday morning.

My dearest Jim,

I heard yesterday that all your photos were received and appreciated. I hope you managed to read Maggie's letter. Her writing baffles me completely and I give up at the first page. They were asking for you, both separately, in stage whispers, and were very anxious to know when you were going to Skelmorlie to pay them a visit, but I think you've a little to do before that.

We had such a jolly lunch – am feeling the effects of eating too much today; we gave them a good menu but I won't make your teeth water by tales of salmon and turkey and all the followers. I was quite hoarse by the evening, had talked far too much of course.

Mrs Wilmer is very progressive having an afternoon whist drive, she seems to move with the times a little. Poor Meg will simply not enjoy it, imagining that Mother Gooding is annoyed seeing her in a new gown out of Falmouth – just as if she will bother – goodness a business needs to be very poor if one has to worry over it to such an extent.

T.H.'s hands are worse again – poor devil – and the cakes have arrived for next week so I must get a note scribbled to her. Meg generally continues to spoil her few pleasures by crossing bridges which have never been built, or are ever likely to, but she must live her own life in her own way I am afraid.

We will be very busy next week. We begin on Wednesday, then the bazaar opens on Thursday, and we'll be there from ten in the morning till eleven at night. So we will be tired all day standing around seeing everybody else is working. Em and I are convenors so have to attend to the responsible parts only.

I have a very sore hand – got Em's stick full weight yesterday and it's the hand that wields the pen.

Pa has given us twenty pounds to divide between the five sisters in Glasgow to spend at it, so we will need to look around and get something worth buying before the decent things are sold.

I am going over to tea with Gerty, Miss Russell, tonight, she's back in her own house now. But is an invalid and is to be very careful all winter – and she finds the evenings very dull and as I am so busy and have no time in the afternoon it suits me very well indeed; she is a dear old soul and is so horribly alone.

Now dear, I seem to have heaps to say but too little space to say it in so I must be "coiling up"! I borrowed that from you.

I wish you were coming for Xmas but no such luck.

I look awful in the group [i.e. one of the photographs] *but then when the original is seen people just say, "Oh! how much lovelier she is than the photo – eh?*

With heaps of love,
Kitty.

Katie's right hand was very painful and badly bruised, but it didn't deter her from helping at the bazaar.

Her next letter was postmarked 4.12.06.

Murcia
Friday Morning

My dearest Jim,

Just got your letter and as I have a few minutes before I need to set forth I will improve the shining hour.

We had a splendid day yesterday, hard work was the order of the day, and we had more than enough of it and were very glad to crawl home about eleven. They had £1000 before the bazaar was opened and I can't say what they made yesterday exactly, as it wasn't in the Herald this morning. But they only wish fifteen hundred so they'll get more than that at least. We drew thirty in the tea room. Em and I had the pay desk to look after and I sold all Meg's cakes quite easily; they were a boon and a blessing.

Of course you don't require to play bridge for money, it's just the same as whist, except that I expect men generally do.

My hand's all right again unless for the look of it, but I never study appearance as you know.

My time is nearly up, I can hear the bugle calling, that is Emma shouting so I must tear myself away. Am sorry to be so scrappy but under the circumstances you will understand, and before concluding, may I add that you need not count the number of words enclosed so that you may write

just as many but no more in return. You've all
Sunday when you're loafing round idling.

So long dear,
Yours lovingly
Kitty.

Katie was puzzled by James' letters which became shorter every time he wrote. She knew of course that he was very busy, but as she pointed out, he had all Sunday to write. She had been somewhat offended too, when he objected to her playing bridge, assuming she had played for money. She was concerned, also, about the number of colds he was getting, and thought that he needed shorter working hours and more outdoor exercise. She did not approve either of the heavy suppers that he ate, because he was prone to indigestion. She was certain that it was supper which caused the problem.

Post mark: 7.12.06.

Murcia
Monday Evening

My dearest Jim,
You seem to be having a busy time although I don't see how you can go any harder than you always go. I don't think you ought to be having so many colds as you get, something must be causing them. Why don't you look after yourself better? I think you are badly needing to be taken in hand by a capable person – me.

My hand is quite painless now so I am quite better. It's all the colours of the rainbow and looks quite interesting.

What a busy time we had, I was so tired on Friday night I couldn't get to sleep. My little trilbies were aching, but it's wonderful how fresh I was on Sunday morning when everything was over. We made £2200, wasn't that good? And our stall made £80 on Saturday. The crowds were so awful I had to stand at the door and keep them back as it was impossible to seat half of them at once. I sold Meg's cakes at once and worked like a galley slave the whole time. I had a little stall of toffee, cakes and a few odds which was killing but I cleaned it out in no time. I just swore every cake was home made – the poorer class seem to fancy that specially – whether it was or not, and so Emma was in a fit at me but I fibbed in a noble cause, to clean a church and get a new organ – the old one is quite exhausted, poor thing! It's very out of date and shows wear, unlike yours truly.

The four convenors have to pay for everything unless a few things we got in donations, so we are just waiting for the bills. The McOnie girls who were with us are very rich and did everything very handsomely – too much so, but one couldn't but admire their generosity, and the majority of our church are pretty poor so we got very little help from the assistants in our room at all.

Poor friend Wilmer – seems laid low, so there is no chance then of you getting a "month" north at Xmas for a little setting up, but the hard work will be the order of the times.

I can't think how you imagine I ever study appearances. I am the simplest of souls and so

263

long as I am covered, I, like the beasts of the field, give no thought as to what I shall put on. I can't get new overcoats, satin lined, like somebody you happen to know pretty well.

I am sorry to hear of Mrs Taylor's bad news. Of course, cancer is beyond all hope. It's a horrible thing.

Who told you Nona's birthday I'd like to know, you take more interest in her than in her sister I am thinking, friend.

Your father is a very sturdy man for his years, he's a little bit of all right if it weren't for mother. She's a pretty hard nut to crack.

Our hockey club has just issued invitations for a fancy dress ball on 17th January; we are inviting over 150 – a good many won't come but we hope a lot will, it's mostly the youthful members who being keen have pushed the thing into shape and I think it will be a great success. The tickets are 5/- fancy dress and 10/- in evening dress, that's to make them come fancy of course.

The curate from Inversnaid is coming to Glasgow to make plans for his bazaar so we will be seeing him likely. I wonder what he looks like in town? Now dear, I guess I've made up for my scrappy epistle – Pa has gone to bed – the fire is going out and it's getting late. Goodbye.

Yours lovingly, Kitty.

From Katie, postmark DEC.14.06.

Murcia
Friday

My dearest Jim,

You must have had plenty to do. I am sorry Mrs Wilmer is so bad, influenza I suppose is a very weakening thing.

I am quite sure you didn't miss your day off a bit – was all I could do to get you to take it in the merry summer which is past.

We have quite recovered from our unusual exertions and having helped to clean a church we feel we can sit down to our Xmas pies with a big "well done."

We were over at Aggie's last night and I got the prize at bridge so am feeling quite inflated, and it's just coming in handy to hand on for Xmas as I don't happen to want it for myself, such doings are far from the simplicity of your remote village when they have progressive whist and no prize at all. Emma thinks it must be a cheap place to live in at that rate.

This place is looking as it used to look a hundred years ago on Christmas cards, covered in snow and a lovely blue sky above. Not having ever seen snow it's difficult for you to imagine.

So you are going to have a tennis dance – it will be very jolly for you and much appreciated by the maidens I expect, down South. I am getting the loan of a Greek costume for ours from Harry's sister. It's too small for her now so I trust I'll create a slight flutter as an Ancient Goddess. Nona says I am ancient enough ...

It doesn't do to take T.H. seriously. He's had such an idle life he must fill in his time some way. Don't you trouble about him.

I am trying to forgive you for daring to write velvet**een**. Of course I saw the "een" scored out, still the idea was there. It's most insulting to my beautiful hat. It's only your sex saves you a severe cuffing – perhaps you'll get it some time.

Pa is going off with some old cronies for the weekend, so we are going to the pantomime tomorrow night.

One sheet doesn't deserve two so goodbye dear. Kitty.

27

James felt beset by troubles on all sides. He was very busy in the dispensary. Mr Wilmer was spending most of the day at home, looking after Mrs Wilmer whose influenza developed into a nasty chest infection. Most nights James didn't finish till well after eight. He had asked his mother if he might take a sandwich down to the shop to eat there, instead of supper at home, but she refused.

In fact, he noticed that Mrs Hocking's attitude to him had changed, and her behaviour had become really rather peculiar. She had taken to staring at him intently, to answering his attempts at conversation brusquely. He could quite see that she was tired because she had to take up the reins of housekeeping again, now that Miss Barley had left, but Connie was proving to be an excellent maid, who had already become quite attached to Mrs Hocking, who, she said, "Does things like my ma does, and runs the house proper."

Added to these burdens was writing twice a week to Katie. By the time he arrived home, had supper and brought in the coal and paraffin ready for the morning, all he wanted to do was to drop into bed. She, who had all the leisure in the world except for tasks which she enjoyed, had hours of time to do as she pleased. He felt hurt that she didn't seem to appreciate his difficulties in the run up to Christmas, what with coughs, colds and influenza, and only he to do all the dispensing.

One Sunday morning, before chapel, he decided to write a longer letter than he had been able to do for some time. He settled down with pen and notepaper at the desk in his bedroom, and had just written "My dear

Katie', when there was a knock at the door, and his mother sailed in.

'Ah, James,' she said, 'I'm glad to have caught you before chapel.'

James stood, covering the beginning of the letter with blotting paper.

'Yes, mother?' he enquired politely, 'What do you want me to do for you?'

She took a small book from her skirt pocket, and thrust it towards him.

'I want you to explain this.'

He stared at the book which she was holding towards him at arm's length.

'This book? Why? What is it?'

'I found it in your summer suit before I sent it to be cleaned. Don't tell me you don't recognise it.'

'Well, I don't.'

'Oh yes you do, James. Take it. Have a look at it.'

He took the book and turned it over. "Callander and the Trossachs".

And then he remembered. Katie had given it to him as they parted at Loch Katrine. Suddenly he felt cold. He looked at his mother. She had a strange and mocking gleam in her eyes.

'You recognise it now, don't you? And don't bother to lie to me as to how you came by it. It was given you, wasn't it? At Loch Katrine? With a sprig of white heather for luck?'

'Yes mother,' he said, putting the book on his desk. 'You are quite right. It was given to me by Katie, to remember a happy holiday.'

He began to feel indignant. He was a man, not a school child to be scolded by his mother.

'I wonder that you were so careless as to leave it for me to find. Or was that intentional?'

'It certainly wasn't. I forgot all about it.'

'Well, I suggest you forget about Miss Carswell and everything to do with her. She is a young hussy James, and she has deliberately led you astray, to the point where you were prepared to deceive your parents.'

'Oh, for goodness sake, mother! All right, I did deceive you, but only because it would have caused such a furore if I'd told you what I intended to do!'

'You fool!'

Her voice, which had been quite soft and level until this moment, seemed to burst from her uncontrollably.

'Just think what you've done to me,' she continued. 'Made your father and me a laughing stock, inveigling the Gravesend family in your shifty little plot, and Edward also, for all I know. And the Clarkes. Why? I'll never be able to look them in the eye again; I'll know they will be laughing behind my back, pitying me for having a son like you.'

He gripped the top rail of the wooden chair he had been sitting on, to stop his hands trembling.

'I'm quite sure they won't mother. I'll – I'll write to them and say you know all the circumstances.'

She drew herself up, almost as tall as he, and furiously angry.

'To go on holiday with a girl like that. Next thing, she'll be writing to you that she's expecting, like as not.'

'Don't be ridiculous. I was invited up there to meet her family, various sisters, and of course Mr and Mrs Sandry who we all know. It was a family holiday – and a very happy one. They're a jolly lot, the Carswells, and the loch and mountains there are simply beautiful.'

'Oh, so the Sandrys know all about it too? I thought her manner was rather strange when I met her in Head's the other day. So now all Falmouth will be buzzing with the gossip about how I was deceived by my own son. You have utterly disgraced us.'

He let go of the chair, moving towards her.

'I'm sorry you feel like this, mother. My only intention was to relieve you of worry.'

She moved forward, staring into his eyes. Her breath was hot on his cheek, her eyes pin points of hatred.

'I shall not forgive this, James,' she whispered. 'I shall speak to your father. And let me tell you that if you marry that girl, we will withdraw our offer of helping you to buy the business.'

She wheeled round and left the room, closing the door a little too firmly behind her.

James sat on the bed. Perspiration was trickling down his cheeks, down his spine. He loosened his collar and tie. What an idiot he had been, leaving the little book to be discovered. How could he have forgotten it? He felt dead tired and in utter despair. She had made him see his happiest holiday ever, as a grubby little deceit.

28

Since her return from Falmouth, Katie had become increasingly concerned about the number of letters she had received from James, and their brevity. She knew very well that he must be exceedingly busy, but had thought that she was important enough to him to warrant him writing a long letter to her on Sundays.

Her uneasiness was not helped by questions from her sisters and friends. One afternoon she, Emma and Winkie were sitting round the fire in the early twilight after a hockey match, drinking tea.

'Have you heard from Falmouth this week?' Winkie asked, suddenly.

'No, not yet,' Katie had replied. 'James is very busy at the moment, he is doing all the dispensing. Mr Wilmer is at home, looking after his wife who's got influenza.'

'More likely James has found another lady friend,' Winkie said, provocatively.

Katie's cup clattered in its saucer. Emma cast a warning glance at Winkie.

'It's quite true, Winkie,' Emma said. 'He's obviously very busy.'

But Winkie was not to be deflected.

'Maybe he is,' she said, 'But he hasn't actually got engaged to you, Katie, has he?'

'Oh that!' said Katie, with a confidence she no longer felt. 'He's getting a lot of his own arrangements out of the way first, buying the shop and so on, then there'll be plenty of time to get engaged and married.'

Nevertheless, Katie was increasingly uncertain as to his intentions, and in her letters repeatedly prodded him to declare himself further.

Emma alluded to these worries a few days later. They were sitting at the breakfast table, having a second cup of coffee, when Bessie brought in the post – one for Emma from the curate, nothing for Katie.

'Is everything all right?' Emma asked, noticing Katie's downcast eyes.

'Not really,' Katie said, 'I'm sure if I could see him, everything would be fine. But it's this everlasting letter writing, we infer meanings that were not intended. We both do it, and then of course, it takes time to explain ourselves and put everything right again. And now he's not even writing.'

'But Katie, he's told you often enough how busy he is at the moment.'

Two tears slid down Katie's cheeks.

'It's not just that,' she said. 'It's that I can't get beyond a certain point. He's sweet and kind and fun, but there's a kind of invisible barrier I never manage to cross.'

Emma sighed.

'Yes, letters are difficult. You can never say what you really think, for words look so bald on paper. I think you'll just have to be very patient. In the New Year he'll be taking over the business, *you'll* get engaged and we'll have to get the house ready for a lovely wedding here in the summer. I know the girls are already planning an archway of hockey sticks for when you come out of church.'

But Katie was not convinced, and her temper rose as she wrote.

From Katie. Post Mark DEC 18. 06

Murcia
Tuesday afternoon

Dear James, You are very busy. I am very sorry that writing to me is such a tax on your spare time, though I don't see your point as you give me quite as little time on Sundays when I expect you are free to do exactly what you choose, but I wouldn't take up more of your time than you care to give and there are numerous things more interesting for you to do.

You will enjoy seeing Edward again – you must take him to Aladdin.

We are not going away this year as the girls are going to London the weekend following New Year and I wouldn't go without Emma, so it will be very quiet as every man, woman and beast goes off for New Year week in these parts.

Bill, Nona and all the clan McCall are going to Bridge of Allan and Winkie is going with them.

I didn't go to the panto: on Saturday as I had gone calling on Friday with Nona, and thinking my fur coat not stylish enough, was too thinly clad for the very severe spell we have just had – and paid very dearly for it as I took violent rheumatics in that shoulder which generally speaks up every wee while. Bessie is rubbing me into smithereens and I managed up this afternoon so hope it will slack off. I've had enough.

*I am sure you will be very busy now so take a holiday. I know I have heaps more time, but you see at this distance Jim "**want inclination**" and "**too busy**" are so nearly related that they seem*

like sisters; two hours in the week doesn't seem to me a great deal to expect, but please yourself.
    Katie.

P.S.   I think three minutes was all you took to the one I got yesterday.

As soon as she had put this letter in the post box at the end of the road, Katie regretted it bitterly. All her anger at his lack of letter writing evaporated. She hovered round the box, praying that the postman would come along to empty the post and that he would allow her to retrieve her letter. It was still bitterly cold, and after half and hour or so, she gave up and went home.

How could she have written those awful things? She knew he was very busy now and that after Christmas work should be a little easier. She remembered how sometimes he went into the shop on a Sunday to make up the stock medicines, or weigh up various powders which were packed into their small white card boxes, for Boracic Powder and Epsom Salts were sold in a range of weights, from quarter pound to one pound boxes.

Flowers of Sulphur, Cream of Tartar and so on were weighed into one and four ounce packets. It was a time consuming job and one which Miss Hawke would do when there were few customers in the shop. As there were no slack periods at present, it made good sense to be beforehand with these tasks.

No doubt James was taking advantage of Sundays to do these essential jobs – working in the stock room and the dispensary which would be cold and miserable without the usual open fire, coals glowing in the grate.

She told Emma what she had done, at teatime. Emma was shocked.

'Why, oh why can't you control your temper? You say you love James, and then you tell me you've deliberately picked a quarrel with him.'

'I know,' Katie said, 'I <u>was</u> very cross and I wrote those things. I just want to know that he loves me but he never says so in his letters.'

'That's very wise of him,' Emma remarked. 'Suppose one of his letters got into the wrong hands?'

'How do you mean?'

Emma poured herself another cup of tea.

'Well, into Mrs Hocking's hands, for a start. And then there's Pa – he'd probably think it wasn't quite the thing for a young man to do.'

Katie sat, staring into the fire, watching the flames licking round the coals.

'I'll write a letter card. With luck it'll get there at the same time as the letter.'

Letter Card Post Mark DEC 19. 06
Please forgive me Jim. I am so sorry – have been thinking myself a beast since I sent it, and don't take a holiday.
Kitty.
Be nice.

James was appalled by the cruel, ill-tempered wording of Katie's letter. He felt beset with troubles in every direction – his mother, the overload of work and now Katie berating him.

After he had finished work that evening, he trudged up the stairs to his old attic room, lit the lamp and roughed out a reply.

275

Dear Katie

I have been rather surprised at your letters lately. I never said it was a tax on my time. I simply said that I was very busy as I certainly was but if you choose not to believe what is told you that has nothing whatever to do with me. It is needless to say that I am very much annoyed at what I consider your very exacting ways and this is only a recurrence of the trouble which took place in the summer when I relieved Mr Wilmer for a short time. I should never have referred to this again only you then promised it should not occur again. You say I must please myself so it appears to me quite immaterial to you whether you receive letters from me or not; but if you can write letters in 3 minutes you are far more clever than I am, I'm quite certain that if I took 3 minutes over my Sunday letter there is as much in my one sheet as you manage on two, very often, as my writing is much more closely written than yours is.

I consider that at this stage you are far too dictatorial as to what I should not do and do not seem to understand at all what business ties mean, especially when one sticks to it and a chemist has to do so, that I am very much afraid you would never be able to put up with such a life.

I am indeed very sorry to hear of your rheumatism and I am sorry to write letters of this kind at this season of the year but if you remember there was something similar about the same time last year. With kind regards. Yours v. sincerely
    James A Hocking.

Katie's hopes dropped like a stone when she read his letter – so he hadn't forgiven her – indeed, his reply only made matters worse. Her shoulder still ached miserably, and altogether she was at a complete loss as to what to do.

She left her breakfast uneaten and went upstairs. She hadn't yet packed his Christmas present. At least she could do that.

She took out the beautiful fair isle waistcoat and scarf which she had bought for him with such pleasure at the bazaar. The wool was gossamer fine, the pattern in shades of burgundy on a dark grey background. She packed them carefully in tissue.

There was a nagging feeling of nausea in the pit of her stomach and her head was aching. Surely, everything would be forgiven and forgotten when he saw this lovely gift? He knew she had a quick temper, regained seconds later. He must know she only wrote that letter in the heat of an exasperated moment?

Sure enough, a letter in the familiar writing came in by the second post of the 22nd December.

Dear Katie

Dec 21. 06

You may as well know that I consider the present state of affairs a very serious one and one not to be trifled with, as the entire happiness of our lives is involved. It's all very well to write one thing one day and the following to write and ask to be forgiven but you must remember confidence is shaken each time and this is not by any means the first time it has happened. Probably had such a thing happened when you were staying here you would have treated me as on one former occasion and sat several hours entirely ignoring my presence. I should not have again referred to this only then you promised nothing of the sort should occur again.

You really must excuse me not being as you call nice but I am not writing this at all unreasonably. How much nicer it would have been and how much more would your regard for me have been shown had you instead of criticising my busy ways expressed sympathy and said if I was busy and unable to find time for the usual length, just to write what I could and you would thoroughly understand. No, I consider you are far too exacting and expect far more than any man who properly attends to his business has time to give. You must not think me hard but I have overlooked the same thing before on several occasions and cannot say I feel quite so amiable on the matter this time.

I am sorry to hear you have an attack of rheumatism but hope that it has quite passed off ere this. With kind regards, Yours sincerely, James A Hocking.

Fortunately Pa had stayed in town for lunch with friends, and Emma pretended not to notice that Katie, pale and silent, ate hardly anything. When Bessie bustled in to collect the plates she was about to remonstrate with Katie, doubtless concerning the waste of good food, when Emma checked her.

Katie jumped up from the table and ran upstairs.

'Oh deary me! What's all this about?' Bessie asked.

'She's had another letter from James. I think she thought that he would forgive her – she'd written too sharply to him you see – but apparently he hasn't. Oh Bessie, whatever shall we do? She's terribly upset and it's nearly Christmas Eve.'

'There's nothing much we can do, Miss Emma. But it's always been the same with Miss Katie, ever since she was a wee bairn she's up in a flame one minute, then away it goes. It seems as if Mr Hocking hasn't realised yet that it's all over in a flash. And she won't change now, I'm thinking. If they're going to get married he'll have to accept that Katie's temper is all part of the Katie we love – bright and cheerful in her ways and as sharp witted as a knife. But I do hate to see her like this. It's not like her to be in this state. Do think if there's anything we can do, Miss Emma, and I'll help you.'

She collected the dishes on her tray and turned to leave the room.

'Don't bother with pudding for me today, thank you Bessie,' Emma said. 'I haven't the stomach for it.'

Katie came downstairs sometime later and together she and Emma wrapped the last of the Christmas presents – their large family meant there were many parcels to tie up ready for everyone's arrival for dinner on the Day. Katie was very quiet, and their conversation consisted of checking for which sister, friend or child each little gift was intended.

At four o'clock Winkie and Harry arrived in a blast of cold air from the front door. They were in excellent spirits, having been shopping in town, and were laden with parcels. Katie greeted them and then, whilst they were showing Emma their bargains, she slipped away

279

upstairs again, fetched her writing box and went into the morning room, where the fire still burned in the grate.

She began her letter.

Post Mark DEC 23. 06.

Saturday Evening.

My dear Jim,

I see that you have not forgiven me. Your letter was a very hard one but I expect I don't deserve any better treatment. I have already said I was extremely sorry so there is no use saying it over again. I know I am exacting where I care very much, perhaps because I do, and in a case like ours where we never meet, I perhaps put too much store by your letters, and knowing that you are influenced against me at home, I can't help feeling that you may be getting indifferent when your letters aren't as nice as I'd like them to be.

I am so miserable since your letter came in that I won't say any more – you know how much I care and if you think you'd be happier with anyone else, I wouldn't stand in your way for a moment, you know that – and if such is the case let me know please. I'd always wish you well, do what will make you happiest.

Whatever's to be, would you let me know soon – Xmas will be a dull time this year for me and if you can't forgive me I'd rather know at once, but please spare me another yours sincerely one, I think I have it by heart. Forgive me entirely or not at all.

Miserably yours
Katie.

December 24th Christmas Eve.

Katie's letter arrived at the shop in the second post. James had been hard at work since eight o'clock, as several people, seeing the lights on inside, had hammered at the door, so he had opened up, then and there, to a steady stream of customers wishing him a "Happy Christmas" with beaming smiles. Some of them extended good wishes to "your Scotch lassie" which only added to the pain he was feeling.

It proved difficult to concentrate on his work, for his thoughts revolved around his love for Katie, and the terrible doubts he now felt about the future.

He read her letter in the dispensary, delaying the next prescription until he'd discovered her feelings. She was "extremely sorry" – "miserable" – she "cared very much" for him – poor little maid.

This heartbroken letter tugged at him, so at lunchtime, instead of going home for his meal, he left the shop and walked up the street to the Post Office.

Here he directed a telegram to Miss K.O. Carswell, Murcia – Glasgow, wishing her a happy Christmas and sending his love.

This done, he returned to the shop, determined that he would leave the question of their future in abeyance over Christmas Day, and would make decisions in the days that followed.

The telegram arrived at Murcia early in the afternoon. Emma and Winkie were doing their best to distract Katie, as they drank coffee after lunch, when they heard the front door bell.

Emma jumped up to answer it. On opening the door, she found an undersized youth in a uniform too large for him, on the top step.

'Telegram for K.O. Carswell, missus,' he said. 'Have I got the right house?'

'You certainly have, thank you,' Emma said. 'Wait a minute.'

She took out some coins, which were always kept ready for tips, from a large Chinese jar which stood on the hall table.

'Thank you,' she said. 'And a happy Christmas.'

'And the same to you missus,' and he ran off down the steps.

Emma hurried into the dining room.

'Telegram for you, Katie.'

Katie stood up, looking paler than ever, and took the telegram.

The others tried not to look at her as she opened the envelope, fearing her reaction. But then:

'Oh, oh', Katie said, her face suddenly pink with joy. 'It's from James. He wishes me a happy Christmas and sends his love.'

Emma and Winkie watched her as she re-read the telegram several times.

'I think everything's all right again,' Katie said eventually, and gave them a dazzling smile.

Half an hour later, Katie took out the tissue wrapped present for James, the fair isle garments, which she hadn't yet sent because of his last letter to her.

She wrote a note:

Murcia
24ᵗʰ December 1906

Dear – thanks so much for your wire. I don't think you will regret sending it. I hope you will wear the enclosed things which gave me such pleasure to get for you, and that your Xmas was a happy one.

Kitty.
It will scratch a little but after the first few wearings it keeps pretty much the same.
K.O.C.

All was well.

29

Edward came home late on Christmas Eve, and on Christmas morning Mrs Hocking insisted that both her boys should go to morning service with their parents. Connie, the new maid, stayed at home to baste the large joint of beef that Mrs Hocking had placed in the oven, with strict instructions on timing to the minute as to when the roast potatoes and Yorkshire pudding should join the meat.

The day passed quietly. In the evening Mrs Hocking announced that carols should be sung, as usual, so they all sang the old favourites, from the Angel of the Lord coming down to the arrival of We Three Kings.

On Boxing Day afternoon, James walked to the station with Edward, who had to return to Dunstable in order to be in time for work next morning.

At Murcia, Christmas Day was joyful and very busy with most of the sisters arriving with their husbands and children for Dinner at two o'clock.

Emma and Katie had laid the dining table, complete with its extra leaves, straight after breakfast, after several countings and re-countings of places needed to be laid. Eventually they settled on twenty five.

The day passed in its normal glory of excitable talk amongst the sisters, as the children stampeded around the house playing Hide and Seek. In the evening there were round games and dances – "The farmer wants a wife," "Here we go round the mulberry bush", all sung at full voice and with the hearty thumping of soles on the wooden floors, until Pa had to retire to his study with a headache.

After Boxing Day, Katie watched the post, at first with hope, and then became ever more anxious when it failed to bring a letter from James.

Emma and Bessie conferred.

'I'm thinking I might send him a wire,' Emma said. 'I'm sure he'd be shocked if he could see the state Katie's in.'

'I know she is, poor wee lamb,' Bessie said. 'A wire, eh? Well, it might just work. It seems so strange that he's not written after the wire he sent on Christmas Eve – we all thought everything was put right then, didn't we? And now the wee lassie is pining away.'

'So – do you think I should?'

'What – send a wire? Well, for sure it can't do any harm and it might set matters right.'

So while Bessie inveigled Katie into the kitchen to make extra mince pies for New Year, Emma hurried to the Post Office to send a telegram to James. In it she stated that Katie was very unhappy and would he please write to allay her fears as soon as possible? Later she told Katie what she had done, but apart from telling her not to interfere, Katie said nothing.

On the 31st December, the long awaited letter dropped through the Murcia letter box. Katie had been hovering in the hall, waiting for the post, and now she scooped James' letter up, leaving the rest of the mail on the hall table.

She ran up to her room and opened the envelope with her nail file – it was a proper, long letter at last.

She read the first lines with delight and relief, but her joy turned to dismay as she read on.

Falmouth Dec 28. 06

Dear Katie,

*Really I scarcely know how to thank you sufficiently for the very lovely present you sent me for Christmas, I only wish the week previous had been so pleasant and I am very sorry I must again refer to it but I feel its quite useless to go farther without setting the matter straight, and please don't think me hard because I'm quite as miserable as you are. I am quite sure that Monday was in every way the **most** miserable and totally wretched day I **ever** spent and there is no doubt that at varying parts of that day I scarcely knew what I was doing and to make matters worse we were so busy and I had to smile and look happy at every customer when in reality my looks so entirely belied my feelings, and at the end of the day I felt that I could not possibly be the cause of a miserable Xmas to a friend, hence the telegram and the present letter is far too important a one to scribble in a hurry.*

You are quite wrong in your surmise as to my thought or care for anyone else; any one who knows me here can truthfully tell you that during our term of correspondence and friendship I have been particularly careful in that matter, so it's entirely your own doing in being so very exacting and suddenly losing your temper which is causing this. Really Katie, I am very disappointed that you write so hurriedly things which are so hurtful and must necessarily wound one's feelings and that there is occasion for me to overlook and forgive so repeatedly. As for forgiving I would do that many

286

times again if I could be quite sure of its non-recurrence.

It's not the present I'm thinking of – it's the future, you must remember when I'm in my own business I shall be far more tied than I am now and shall have all the responsibility and if I am not able to satisfy your requirements now how much more difficult will it be then, so there are all these things to be thought of, and after a man has been in business all day he wants to come back to his home, not to find his friend cross because he has been kept unavoidably for an extra quarter of an hour but rather to sympathise with on that account especially a sensitive disposition like the one in question.

You say there is undue influence at home with my people but that is not so in this case; I own and you know I am very sorry that it has been the case on former occasions but cannot blame them this time.

You are very large hearted in wishing me to do whatever will make for my happiness but I'm so afraid (and I can scarcely expect) that you'll never like my people and being the eldest son I shall be obliged to manage a great deal for them and one of the things which would make me very unhappy would be continual friction which is so terribly personified in George Penlerick's case. Of course I am quite willing to admit and have done so all along that my folks are very unfair but provided they should for my sake become different and I believe they would in time, it seems to me scarcely possible to ask you to overlook past slights and be the same as though nothing had happened, and the attitude which you took last week and have done

287

on former occasions makes the thing appear more impossible.

I have been very anxious that you should fully realise my future position and if we are so often squabbling now at this early stage whatever will things be like in a few years time?

Personally I don't quite understand the caring for one so much that on the slightest provocation says they may please themselves whether they will or not and take a holiday and so on, you could not have cared a great deal when you wrote that.

*Now Katie, I sincerely hope I shall not lose your friendship. I don't wish to do that, but perhaps while I am busy about the business transfer and shall not have a great deal of spare time and you may be thinking it is intentional, we had better write casually instead of regularly twice a week as we have been doing. I take it as a very serious matter that we are so often having rows and am rather distressed about it, I should be glad to know how you feel abut the matter, but it seems to **me** the only course to take. I am indeed sorry to propose this and if you feel it at all you cannot be sorrier about it more than I shall. Remember, I shall still hope to hear from you but I never want another week like I have had this week. It would have been so much better if we could have had a chat.*

Goodbye, with love from Jim.

She sat, for an hour or more, in the cold bedroom, occasionally checking what he had actually written in various parts of the letter, but she could not really believe that all their love and friendship had come to this. And he had written out the real root of the problem, she was sure, for she well knew that a chat would soon put everything right.

Nevertheless she could not understand the cold, dispassionate way that he wrote, sentence after sentence, dissecting their relationship, using instances of her behaviour that she had forgotten abut. Perhaps this was the worst of all – his preparedness to nurse a grudge. She knew that she was far too quick tempered – goodness, Emma and the family had told her so often enough – but this cold, calculating way of recalling her every mistake was a perspective new to her, one that she had not encountered before.

Although he stated that his parents had not influenced his thinking, Katie had a strong suspicion that something had occurred – something that his mother had said, for the language in this letter seemed very much at odds with his usual warm and sincere style. She could not imagine what had caused this outburst, and was aware that in all probability she would never know.

How to reply? Beg him again to forgive her? Promise never again to constrain him in anything? How could she possibly write to him casually, and as casually await a reply?

No, their loving friendship had gone much too far to make stepping back a possibility.

At that moment there was a tap on the door. It opened a little way and Emma looked in.

'May I come in?' she asked.

'If you wish.'

Emma came to sit beside her on the bed.

'Not good?'

At first Katie didn't reply, and then suddenly she turned towards her.

'It's all over, Em. He wants us to go back to writing to each other, occasionally, just friends. And I can't do that. We've got to a stage which makes that absolutely impossible. We've talked about marriage often. I know the pitfalls. I know he has to work long hours. I've promised to try to like his horrible mother. But it's no good. He says it's not because of influence at home, but what else could it be?'

They sat in silence for a while. Then Emma said:

'Couldn't you do as he suggests and try writing casually? You would keep the friendship going, and later when the shop business has been resolved, and it's spring again – well, then your letters can get warmer and more regular again.'

'I can't Emma. It wouldn't happen like that. No. I'm sure his mother is at the bottom of this.'

Unable to help her, Emma left her and went downstairs, leaving Katie's door ajar.

Wearily, Katie opened her writing box, picked up her pen and began to write.

Murcia
31ˢᵗ Dec 1906

Dear Jim,

I got your letter this morning though I had given up expecting one.

Emma told me yesterday that she wired you last week, she hadn't any business to but as she meant well there's no use saying anything to her.

I couldn't possibly be more miserable than I have, so that your letter leaves me as it found me. It's a very hard one and that I deserve a good deal of it doesn't make it less so by any means.

290

I don't think you are quite fair. It never occurs to you to think that what you refused to do in the Autumn mattered to me, but I only asked you because all my people thought you ought, and constant questionings are irritating even when it's only sisters.

You ask me what I think on the writing subject. You are simply breaking my heart Jim, it's absolutely impossible for me to treat you as an acquaintance; if it's possible to you there's no use my saying anything. More on the point, what I went through last week, expecting one by every post would be quite impossible, I couldn't stand it. I can't nurse resentment for weeks. You are too hard and I am terribly miserable.

You know I promised you I'd never bear your people any ill will, not through any love for them, but because I cared for you, so I think your attack on that quarter is very unmerited, as the only occasion I ever got I showed no resentment whatever.

However it's not that that matters, it's yourself. Half a loaf is not better than no bread. Jim, I can't stand it. If you care then care, but don't send me another such as today's. I will never exact anything from you again, you needn't have doubts about that, but if we are to be friends then it must be on the same footing.

If you ever realised how hard it was never to see you, you'd write a kinder letter – am too unhappy to write more.

Katie.

She didn't read through the letter, merely folded it and pushed it into an envelope, found two green halfpenny stamps and stuck them on. She ran down the stairs, forgetting coat, hat and gloves, opened the front door and rushed down the steps.

Emma was in the drawing room doing a little unnecessary dusting whilst waiting for Katie to appear again. At last she heard her running down the stairs; within moments she heard the front door slam, and she hurried to the window in time to see Katie, letter in hand, flying down the steps onto the pavement, ill clad for such a cold day.

But it was her desperate expression that alarmed Emma more than anything. Katie had looked grief-stricken. Emma dropped her duster and rushed to put on her coat and a warm shawl round her head and shoulders, and followed Katie down the street, moving more slowly than Katie, just keeping her in sight.

She saw Katie reach the post box, where she hesitated, looking down at the envelope for some moments, and then thrusting it into the box.

Emma continued to walk along the pavement, expecting Katie to turn and come back, but she didn't. Instead she seemed to embrace the stout Victorian post box, seemed to be trying to grasp it. Emma quickened her step.

Then to her dismay she saw Katie slipping, slithering down from the box to sink on to her knees and then to crumple into a small heap on the ground.

Emma ran. She knelt beside Katie and put her arms round her shoulders.

'Katie, Katie,' she said urgently. 'Katie. I'm here. It's all right. It's Emma, Katie.'

She was frightened. Katie's face was a greyish white. She touched her ice cold cheek, then pulled off her shawl and wrapped it round her sister's head and shoulders.

'It's Emma, Katie. Here's my shawl – just round your shoulders. Katie, can you hear me?'

To her intense relief, Katie turned her head towards her and opened her eyes. They took a little time to focus.

'Katie. It's me, Emma.'

Katie stared at her.

'Oh Em,' she said. 'I'm sorry. I'll be all right again in a minute.'

'Take your time,' Emma said. 'There's no hurry.'

'Can you help me to get up? My knees are all shaky.'

At last Katie seemed sufficiently recovered to be lifted up and supported by Emma's arm. With her arm firmly round her, Emma was shocked to feel how thin she had become; she could feel every rib beneath her fingers.

The street had been quite deserted, but now Emma heard the clip clop of hooves and smooth running wheels, which came to a halt alongside them. It was Pa, returning home for lunch.

'Good gracious girls!' he said. 'Whatever's happened?'

He didn't wait for an answer, but jumped down to take Katie's weight from Emma.

'Come on. Let's get you home. It's too cold to be lying about on the pavement.'

Between them, and with the help of the cabbie, they lifted Katie into the cab and onto a seat, and set off up the street.

Once home, Emma called Bessie to bring up two hot water bottles, and took Katie up to her bedroom.

Soon she was in bed accompanied by the stoneware hot water bottles, and Bessie was laying and lighting the bedroom fire.

'Would you like something to eat, Katie? It's lunch time remember. And mind you don't kick those bottles out.'

'Just a cup of tea please.'

In the absence of Bessie, Cook had taken up today's casserole and potatoes so that Pa could have his lunch before returning to town.

Emma came into the dining room a little later.

'How is she?' asked Pa.

'A better colour, poor wee thing. But she's just so sad, Pa.'

'The Falmouth fellow?' he asked.

'Yes, I'm afraid so. He's called everything off.'

'Has he indeed? Jilted my daughter? Oh, I know "jilted" is a hard word Emma, but that's what he's done. Look after her. I'll speak to her tomorrow when she's feeling better.'

**JANUARY
1907**

30
January
1907

Pa did not follow his usual routine next morning. Instead, he asked Bessie to light a fire in his study, and after breakfast retired there to examine *The Scotsman*. The morning's news scanned, he requested Bessie, who had come in to stoke up the fire, to send Katie in to see him when she had finished her breakfast.

Katie, startled, presented herself at the study door, somewhat apprehensively. What could Pa possibly want?

'Ah, Katie, there you are. Come in and sit down. I want to talk to you.'

'Yes Pa?'

Pa folded the newspaper and placed it on his desk.

'Are you feeling better today? You seem to have a bit more colour in your cheeks.'

'Yes Pa, thank you. I'm all right today. I really don't know what came over me.'

'Well, for one thing, my lass, you had insufficient warm clothing. Running out in a blouse and skirt in this weather! Why you young people refuse to dress in sensible winter clothing I simply don't understand. Folks die of the cold, but the young seem to think they're impervious. And are you eating your porridge?' he asked, cunningly changing his tactics.

'Sometimes, Pa.'

'That's not good enough. Start the day with porridge and you're well set up. But that's not why I want to speak to you.'

He noticed the dismay on Katie's face, but pressed on with the interview. He'd never been a man to shirk difficult duties, and he was not going to begin today.

'Now Katie. I don't want to know all the whys and wherefores, but you have been looking very wan lately – no Christmas spirit at all.'

'No – I'm sorry, Pa.'

Pa picked up the paper knife from his desk, balancing it on his index finger.

'So what has been the cause of this melancholy?'

He waited, but she didn't reply.

'Am I right in supposing it's trouble with the Falmouth man?'

He thought he heard Katie breathe yes.

'And you've between you decided that you're not suited?'

Katie cleared her throat.

'James decided Pa. But it's mostly my fault. He says I'm too exacting and,' she dropped her voice, 'bad-tempered.'

'Indeed? So he's jilted you – you know what that means, I daresay?'

'Yes Pa. There's another thing too. His parents, especially his mother, don't like me. His mother was dead set against me.'

Mr Carswell replaced the knife on the desk.

'I see. And this has made you very unhappy?'

'Yes Pa.'

Tears began to gather in her eyes, he noticed. Then a spark jumped out of the fire and landed on the carpet. Mr Carswell leapt up and stamped on it, then turned towards her, his back enjoying the heat of the fire.

'Listen to me, Katie. You won't like me saying this, but in a few weeks, or perhaps months, you'll admit I am right. All this is very painful now, but time and distance

298

will ease the pain. Always remember that we are CARSWELLS, and Carswells hold their heads high – we're proud people. Don't let anyone see you care. Put a cheerful face on it – that's my advice.'

Katie's eyes had been downcast, but now she looked up at him.

'I'll try, Pa. But it's very hard.'

He took his hunter watch from his waistcoat pocket, checking the time with the grandfather clock in the corner.

'Now. I've been thinking. There's another thing. You're a bright wee lass, able to do all the French translation in the office, for example. I think you need more to do than helping Emma in the house and banging about with hockey sticks and tennis bats.'

'Racquets, Pa.'

'Eh, yes? Well, don't interrupt me. You should be making use of your brain, taking a course of study. What do you say?'

Katie seemed diverted by this idea.

'How do you mean, Pa? I'm no bluestocking. You know that.'

'Good heavens preserve me from daughters who are bluestockings. But look about you, see if there's anything you'd like to study.'

He was pleased to see that his stratagem had diverted her; already he could see she was considering possibilities.

'Perhaps I could become a suffragette?' she asked, gazing at him innocently.

'Over my dead body,' he roared predictably. 'In the meantime, Bill will be away again in February, so be ready to come down to the office to help with the French.'

'I will Pa, and thank you.'

The season had passed quietly. The streets around them had been busy with cabs and carriages piled with trunks and boxes, for the previous few days, as everyone departed for their New Year holidays.

Katie, Emma and Pa were left at home, Winkie, Nona and Bill, and Harry having all gone to London.

Despite all that had happened, Katie still hoped against hope that James would relent. However, the letter arriving on Jan 4th was conclusive:

Wodehouse Terrace
Falmouth

Jan 3.07

Dear Katie,

Your letter of 31st now to hand, from which I learn that you are very unhappy; well now does it never occur to you that there is a possibility of my being quite as unhappy as you are, and if unhappiness is ours now at this point, whatever is the future to be?

So Katie I am sorry to say you have entirely destroyed the implicit confidence I had put in you and once that happens it seems to me that everything else is at an end. The matter you speak of in your letter is not the one I referred to. If you remember one evening in summer you distinctly told me that I might go where I was more required or something to that effect. Viz that time on a certain Friday when I relieved Mr Wilmer for a few hours, and after I came back you sat for an hour or two having nothing to say to me, and when we made that matter right, you promised it should not again occur. But I consider the question now in hand is almost precisely of the same nature and it seems to me that our friendship has been a series of offences and forgiveness of the same, but I feel the present one cannot be overlooked and I fear that having had so many rows as we have had – it clearly points to the unsuitability of the two individuals concerned.

With kind regards,
Yours sincerely,
James A. Hocking.

So that was it – the end of all her hopes, her love and all their happy plans dismissed. Hopelessness enveloped her all the rest of that day.

But next morning she awoke to snowlight stealing around the edges of her blue velvet curtains. She sat up in bed. There was a tap on the door, and Bessie entered, carrying a tray of tea.

'Oh, you're awake. That's better.'

She bustled over to the windows and drew back the curtains revealing bright sunlight reflected on another snowfall. Church bells were pealing for early service.

Despite her sadness, Katie felt heartened. She drank her tea, washed and dressed quickly, and ran down to the warmth of the morning room. After breakfast, she decided, she would write the letter, keeping Pa's words in the forefront of her thoughts.

Accordingly she fetched her writing box and began.

Murcia
Sunday

Dear James

Thank for your letter. I quite agree with you that we are quite unsuited and I sincerely hope you will have no unhappiness on my account.

You are too good. I am of the world worldly and have never moved in a narrow grove [sic]. You will get a far better girl across the border.

Let me assure you I do not regret our past friendship, it has done neither of us any harm and at the parting of the ways I sincerely wish you every good luck.

*I am writing Meg to tell her that we **mutually agreed** to differ so that they may know you are in no way to blame but have been honourable throughout.*

I know I can trust in your honour as a man to burn every line I ever wrote you as I have already done. I am posting on the bracelet, the only thing left. Will you burn what I sent you at Xmas or sell them and give the money to any needy soul you happen to be interested in, as I never wish to hear from you in any way again.

Believe me.
Yours v. sincerely
Katie O. Carswell.

She didn't seal the envelope immediately, but re-read her words at several intervals during the day.

After breakfast next morning, she took the letter down to the post box and pushed it through the slit, hearing its hollow fall onto other letters below. Her eyes welled with tears, but she swept them away with her handkerchief, and on impulse, decided to go on into town.

She walked briskly, feeling better with every step on this crisp, cold morning. She'd go into Pa's office and get one of the errand boys to go up to Murcia, with a note explaining where she was.

That done, she joined the crowds and window-shopped along the streets. She was mindful of Pa's words, that she should look for something to occupy her. That was all very well if you were burning with some great ambition, but she had been very happy with the life she'd led, which of course had included James. Now that dream was shattered, where was she to go?

She paused outside the window of a fashionable dress shop, scanning the trends for the New Year, and then moved on. She was no longer interested. Then she noticed a neat plaque on the next doorway.

'Mrs McClure's Type Writing School for Young Ladies', she read. She began to move on, then stopped, and turned back. Type writing?

She opened the door and entered.

She stood in an empty hall with closed doors on all sides. Each door bore the name of a different company. An arrow pointed up the stairs: TYPEWRITING, FIRST FLOOR.

As she climbed the stairs the clack and rattle of a dozen typewriters grew ever louder. Someone was counting loudly to a steady beat. At frequent intervals a dozen bells rang and the voice called some command and off they went again. She stood outside the door and listened. Could she? It would be a start.

She opened the door and approached the reception desk.

***

James came home as usual for lunch and scanned the hall table for post. There was nothing for him.

He had gone up to the attic at the shop and packed Katie's last letter into the Elliman's Embrocation box. It was full now, he noted – full of all those letters she had written to him. 'Burn them.' she had said, but he hadn't the heart to destroy them – not yet, anyway. They were the only remaining link with that joyful time they had shared.

He had thought as he wrote that last letter to her, finishing it all, that he would feel unburdened, a great relief, one responsibility off-loaded. But all he felt now was a dull ache; he felt empty, utterly cheerless. There would never be any more Glasgow letters, loving, infuriating, newsy letters dropping on to the shop door mat.

Mrs Hocking came into the hall as he was taking off his coat.

'Ah, James,' she said. 'No post for you.'

'I know, I've just looked', he said. 'But I had a letter from the solicitors this morning. They're now ready to go ahead to completion on the purchase of the shop.'

'Well that's good news,' she said, adding sourly, 'and without doubt your Glasgow friend will be delighted.'

She took his coat, shaking off the rain drops, and hung it on its customary hook.

'You may as well know, mother,' James said, 'that my friendship with Katie is at an end.'

She swung round to face him. A slow triumphant smile animated her heavy face. She stepped towards him, opened her arms to embrace him!

'My dear boy,' she began ...

James stared at her, uncomprehending, and then realisation came crashing over him like a wave, and he knew that he had made a terrible mistake.

He turned and left the house, welcoming the rain and the cold air on his face. He reached Market Strand and ran up the stairs to the quiet security of his attic room.

THE END

Epilogue

During 1907, James' purchase of the shop was successfully concluded. In the box is a rough sketch of the new sign board, drawn by James on a scrap of paper.

It must have been a proud day for him when the board was erected, and a small photograph records the new look to the shop.

His parents died during the next few years.

In 1917 he married Mabel Bray in London. They made their home at Grovelands, Western Terrace, Falmouth. A baby girl was born in 1918 and a second girl in 1921.

On August 17th 1922, James and Mabel went, with a group of friends, to a concert in the Princess Pavilion. Afterwards, the party returned to Grovelands for supper. In the early hours of the 18th, James was awoken by a terrible chest pain. He died before Dr Trail could reach him. He was 44.

The Falmouth Packet reported his death on that same sad morning. It mentioned the shock of sorrow which pervaded the town, for James was now a well-known and well-loved member of the community, meticulous in his work and helpful to the many people who trusted and consulted him.

It is tempting to wonder if the indigestion, which was a recurring theme in his correspondence with Katie, was in fact angina, for his death certificate states that he died from Angina Pectoris and Cardiac Failure.

And Katie? Katie never married. Her Pa died in 1910, which must have caused a considerable upheaval in her life. She died in Worthing, Sussex in 1962. She was 84.